The Gift Healers

REBECCA MILLANE

First published in 1995 by
Brandon Book Publishers Ltd,
Dingle, Co. Kerry, Ireland

Copyright © Rebecca Millane 1995

British Library Cataloguing in Publication Data is available for this book

ISBN 0 86322 210 2

Typeset by Seton Music Graphics, Bantry, Co. Cork
Cover design by Design Associates, Tralee, Co. Kerry
Printed by ColourBooks Ltd, Dublin

Contents

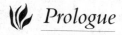 *Prologue*

SOME YEARS AGO a baby boy was born to Ellen and Edward McDonagh in the Regional Hospital, Galway. He was christened Simon Christoper, but that was later.

While he was still only a few hours old, an older ritual was carrried out. A young trainee nurse ran outside and turned over a couple of stones in the grassy patch beside the driveway. She returned to the ward and quickly and unobtrusively placed a tiny worm on the infant's palm, then traced a circle around it with her finger.

Instantly the worm stopped wriggling. It was dead.

The young woman, training to take her place in modern high-tech medicine, and the tired older woman, the baby's mother, hugged each other in the joy of the age-old discovery. 'He has the cure. He has the cure,' they rejoiced.

Simon is a seventh son, and there is a traditional belief in Ireland that a worm must be placed in such a child's hand before baptism, to ensure that he will have the cure for ringworm. In fact Simon now cures many other things.

He is eleven years old now. A strong, handsome boy, he is, according to his mother, as wild as a little hare. I asked him how he felt about his gift. He was sitting beside me on a couch – well, bouncing would be a more accurate description.

'I love doing it, because the more I do it the more people will come to me, and the better I'll be getting.'

What does it feel like? I asked him.

'Well, you know how, in the morning when you wake up, you go like that?' – he stretched out his arms. 'Well, when I go like that,' Simon went on, 'I get a pain in my arms, and you feel the power going through your arms into your hands. You know, like that.'

I didn't know. What kind of power? I asked.

'You know, power, just like God, just like God coming through you.'

Simon worked his first cure when he was eleven months old. His mother Ellen told me about it:

'An old man, who knew me since I was a child myself, heard I had a seventh son. He asked me if Simon could cure eczema. The man had been in the hospital and they couldn't cure him. He was covered with it.

'I told him the child was very young, not even a year old, and that I didn't know if he could do anything. I said I'd chance it, and the poor man opened his shirt and you never saw anything like the state he was in. I rubbed the child's little hand on him and the poor man was afraid for the child and would only barely let me touch him. I didn't know what the prayer should be, so I just said three Hail Marys and the Our Father.

'He came back the second time and it had gone whitish, and after the third time it was gone.'

About this time a young girl with ringworm on her leg came to the house. Again Ellen explained that Simon was only a baby, but she tried it, rubbing the affected spot with the baby's hand. Again she said prayers, worrying that it might not be right for her to say them, as they should be said by the child.

The girl was completely cured.

Those were the beginnings, and it has gone on until by now the eleven-year-old Simon is well known as a healer in his locality. I pressed Ellen to tell me what else he can cure.

'There's this man in Cavan,' she told me, 'Christy Coyne is his name – a healer. He was born with the gifts of curing diarrhoea and pain in the back. Now, if a person with cures meets another healer with the same name, they can share their cures. My little lad is Simon Christopher, so Christy Coyne could give him a cure. He taught Simon how to do the cure for diarrhoea and he told him the prayer. Simon was never to tell that prayer to anyone else.

'The cure? He boils milk and reddens a poker and puts it into the milk. Then he skims off the top of the milk and gives it to the person to drink, and says the prayer. They get cured of the diarrhoea.'

Casually Ellen added: 'He can cure gastritis, too.'

I asked how he does it.

'Well, I asked him to try it, to help the people who came asking. So he does the same as for diarrhoea and it cures it.'

Did Christy Coyne give him the gift of curing back pains as well? I asked. She said he did, and that Simon can cure that too. How does he do it? I asked.

'Well, he leaves his little foot on the place in the person's back. I suppose any kind of a pain in the back, I don't know.'

His foot? I asked. Why his foot?

'That's what Christy Coyne told him to do.'

So far, it seemed everything Simon does has been told or taught to him by others. Does he have cures that come completely from himself? Has he an independent awareness of his gifts?

'Oh, yes. He knows he can cure all sorts of rashes. I don't know how he knows, but he does know. He even knows what he can't cure. He'll tell you that if it's the eczema that goes into the blood, he can't cure it. He always knows when he sees a rash if he can cure it. The doctors get it very hard to cure the dry eczema – the one that comes out in blistery spots and things. Simon cures that: he puts his little hand on it and blows on it.'

'Do you find it all extraordinary?' I asked Ellen.

'Oh, I do, and I know it's a lovely gift to have. His mind is bet down on the cure.'

Later Simon added his own twist to the puzzle. He cannot cure on Tuesdays. He has found that his cure simply will not work on Tuesdays, so he asked people to come on any day but then.

<hr />

Every year in Ireland about 20,000 people go to healers like Simon, looking for cures for an extraordinary range of things: cures for burns, brucellosis, skin cancer, bleeding. And many claim to be cured.

This book is about such healers. It is not about chiropractors or homeopaths or that whole sector of alternative medicine – those who have developed unorthodox skills and knowledge to put at the service of the sick. The healers in this book are different: they claim neither special training, knowledge nor skills, but a gift from God. Or from nature. Or from inheritance. Or passed on from someone else. Ultimately they do not know whence the gift comes, but it is usually a gift to cure something specific.

They are not faith healers either. An infant who heals can hardly be said to have faith. Some of these can heal people thousands of miles away who are not even aware of them, much less have faith in them. Faith healers rely exclusively on prayer and faith: these do not. The phenomenon of these healers is comparable with water diviners, in that they use a gift that nobody can begin to understand, yet many avail of.

There are many such healers in Ireland. I call them 'gift healers'. For this book I have sought out some of the best known and most respected. I have visited them, talked with them into the small hours, watched them as they heal, talked with those who come seeking cures and with those who claim to have been cured – all to try to understand what these gifts are.

I may as well say at the start that I have failed. The mystery gets deeper and deeper the closer you get to it. The more you know of these gift healers, the more baffled you become. No one seems able to offer an explanation for their extraordinary abilities. I talked with physical scientists, medical practitioners, theologians – and they all say, quite simple, *we do not know.*

However, I can also say this: the more baffling this mystery grows, the more fascinating it becomes. 'There are more things in heaven and earth, Horatio, than are dreamt of in your philosophy.'

❦ *In Search of Healing*

HUMANKIND IS HAUNTED by pain. If the story of that pain and the search for relief could be told in full, it would show a truer picture of humanity's journey than is shown by conventional history. Truer, because it would be about all people, about childbirth and leprosy, toothache and burns, blindness and wounds and strokes and paralysis and cancer, and about what could be done about them. It would not be just about kings and generals and battles, invasions and emperors and popes, pomp and looting and defeat and victory and massacres. It would be about curing rather than killing.

Here in the Western world, coming up to the third millennium, we have a scientifically based medicine which can control most pain and cure much illness. We understand more than our ancestors did about the causes of illness, from hygiene to diet to lifestyles. We can conquer most infection, while organ transplants and heart bypasses have come off the pages of science fiction right into everyday life. With all this power to heal, we are freed from the terrors that enslaved our ancestors. We pay no tolls to the spirits of pools or rocks or forests. We have forgotten the evil eye. We fear neither gods nor demons. We reject the notion of hidden powers.

Or do we?

Our self-assurance would seem to be limited to those areas of life which are based on proven scientific truths and values. In other areas of life, where we do not always have full control or full understanding, we are not always so assured.

In 1990, during the early days of the Gulf War, a good-looking, pretty, well-dressed, sophisticated and evidently educated young woman was seen on TV screens around the world. She was waiting for a plane carrying some of Saddam Hussein's hostages back to London.

'Who are you meeting?' a reporter asked.

'My husband,' was the reply.

The reporter persisted: 'Are you sure he's on board?'

'No,' she replied, 'but I've got my fingers crossed.'

Two thousand years ago a woman in Gaul, waiting to see if her prisoner husband would be released by triumphant Caesar, might have made precisely the same gesture, used the same words.

On 1 November 1991, journalist Robert Fisk was talking on Radio Teilifís Éireann (RTE, Ireland's national broadcasting service) about angry exchanges between Syria and Israel.

'So what will US foreign secretary James Baker do tomorrow?' the interviewer asked.

'Cross his fingers,' was Fisk's reply.

A few days later a man wrote to RTE radio presenter Gay Byrne about a series of misfortunes that had recently befallen a friend. He wondered if his friend were not the victim of a curse.

So what is going on? It would seem that these 'superstitions' come from inherited beliefs, rejected at an intellectual level, but so deeply ingrained that they function in an almost automatic, arbitrary way, and cut across differences in race, age, education and religion. We are talking about magic. Magic has kept its grip on the imaginations and emotions of people longer than any recorded religious, dynastic, military or democratic system. Where civilisations have marched, magic has crept, step by soft step, adapting, accommodating itself, surviving – always surviving. It whispers of secrets, hints at mysteries and knowledge, promises power, and is woven into the fabric of our lives. Its origins are lost in time.

People scoff, saying all of that went out with the flood, but it didn't. Magic has been tamed, laundered, even deodorised. The wild has been fenced out. But that is all.

This book recounts how every day in modern Ireland hundreds of people visit these gift healers, seeking relief through their hidden and little-understood powers. We can call it magic if we wish. Or we can call it faith. Or we can call it a natural or God-given gift. We can call it anything we like, but people continue to go, and, regularly, they claim to be cured after a session with one of these healers.

When we look back to the past, at how deeply beliefs in such powers – for both hurting and healing – were ingrained in everyday life, it is not surprising that such beliefs do not simply wither away. This book looks at the people who heal according to such beliefs, and examines the remarkable powers they seem to have.

But first, the past.

The ancients in many parts of the world saw illness as a consequence of evil spirits entering the human body. They also believed that some people had the evil eye, and could cause injury, ill luck, illness or even death, merely by glancing at another person. Some possessors of the evil eye

deliberately used their power to harm; others seemed un-
aware of their unhappy gift. Both kinds were called *jettatori*
in Italian.

People of the evil eye came from all walks of life: even
the papal throne gave no immunity. The nineteenth-
century Pope Pius IX was reputed to be a *jettatore*. According to Thomas Elworthy,[1] everything the pope touched
became a fiasco. In the 1843 campaign against Austria, the
Italians were winning battle after battle, 'when suddenly he
blessed the cause and everything went to the bad at once'.

Poor Pius IX was simple bad news. 'Nothing succeeds
with anybody or anything when he wishes well to them,'
according to a contemporary. When he arrived in St Agnese
to hold a great festival, the floor of the church collapsed and
the people were crushed together. He visited the column to
the Madonna in the Piazza di Spagna in Rome and blessed
the workmen; one fell from the scaffold that very day and
died. He arranged to meet the king of Naples, when up
came a violent gale and a storm that lasted a week.

An English nobleman was unwell at Albano: the pope
sent his blessing and the man promptly died. 'There was
nothing so fatal as his blessing,' Elworthy says. Workmen in
Rome simply refused to work unless the pope stayed away
from the site.

These episodes emphasise that a belief in the evil eye was
alive and well in the mid-nineteenth century. Furthermore,
belief in protection against it and remedies for it were also
very much to the fore, as they had been down the centuries.

As far back as the ancient Egyptians, amulets were
viewed as standard protection against the evil eye. People
wore them to protect both themselves and their dead.
These amulets usually bore an image of the scarab beetle or
the eye of the god Osiris, ruler of the underworld.

Even today, many Muslims embroider sentences from the Koran on to their clothes to guard against the evil eye. All over the world, the way to counter the evil eye was to point two fingers at the possessor. The gesture was known as 'The Horns'. There are extant drawings of a North American Indian helmet carrying horns, seemingly for the same purpose.[2]

If this response to the evil eye was protective and self-defensive, there was also healing magic which was active and vital, even aggressive. Its enemy was the whole race of demons and evil spirits that attacked humanity, causing illness, injury and death. It followed that, since the disease was the work of demons, the physician had to be skilled in magic lore, be capable of identifying the particular demon and exorcising it, thereby restoring the patient to health. The methods used to expel demons were as varied as the demons themselves. One method was to make a clay figure, into which the demon was inveigled to enter. The magician then destroyed the figure by burning, and the victim would, it was hoped, be restored to health.

C.J.S. Thomas describes three classes of exorcists in ancient Mesopotamia – seers, priests and chanters. The seers consulted the gods and foretold the outcome from the entrials of animals or the flight of birds. The priests and chanters exorcised by incantations and by making offerings – of honey, butter or garlic.

The recovery rate among unwell Mesopotamians might not have been very high, but we should not regard the ancients with pity: they may have lacked science, but not intelligence or integrity, and they were familiar with powerful drugs like mandrake, opium, and hellebore that are still used today. Admittedly they could not control infection, but neither could modern medicine until Fleming discovered penicillin in 1928.

Another form of healing was healing by sympathy, which reached its high point in the sixteenth and seventeenth centuries. If a person was injured by a sword, the *sword* would be anointed so that the victim would heal. The wound was more or less ignored, except perhaps for occasional cleaning.

The practice probably gained wide credence because of the eminence of those who advocated it, for example, Paracelsus, the Swiss physician who is also credited with improving pharmacy, encouraging scientific experiments and generally revolutionising medicine. In fairness it should be noted that he directed that wounds should be covered. The Church held that sympathetic cures were the work of the devil and they were completely discredited in 1773 when Antoine Baumé, eminent French scientist, denounced their claimed successes as illusory.[3]

Sympathetic magic had its dark side. It was also used to cause illness, and even death. For example, in the Pitt Rivers Museum at Oxford is a clay figure representing an actual man whose death it was meant to invoke. Made as recently as 1889 in Glen Urquhart in Scotland, it would have been placed facing the victim's house, whereupon the victim would die.[4] The antiquity of this mode of working evil is evinced by the discovery at Thebes of a similar clay figure, tied to a papyrus scroll carrying the name of the man who was to die. It is now in the Ashmolean Museum in Beirut.[5]

Nearer home, St John Seymour tells of an incident on one of the Aran Islands, when the local doctor had given up hope of assuaging the illness of a man sick from an incurable disease. 'After a struggle with his conscience, he sought the services of a *cailleach* who had the power to transfer mortal sickness. . . The *cailleach* would go out to some field near a road, and, setting herself on her knees, she would pluck a herb from the ground, looking out on the road as she did so. The first passerby that her baleful glance lighted on would take the sick man's disease and die of it in twenty-four hours, the patient mending as the victim sickened and died.'[6]

There is another extraordinary example of a method used for what can only be termed unsympathetic magic. It is both malign and blasphemous. The ill-wisher goes to the church and, back turned to the altar, utters certain words. He or she then shapes a sheaf of wheat like a human body, sticking pins in the joints, and buries the sheaf in the name of the devil near the house of the victim. Bury the sheaf in wet ground where it quickly decays, and the victim dies fast. Bury it in dry ground where decomposition is slow, and the victim lingers in pain. A case in which one woman tried to kill another by this means came to light in the police court at Ardee, County Louth, in 1892.[7] Witchcraft in fact was recognised officially in Ireland as a legal offence until 1951, when it was dropped from the Fraudulent Mediums Act.

The method known as the Doctrine of Signatures was another ancient system of healing, though its origins are uncertain. It was based on the belief that some plants, or parts of them – leaves, roots, juice – resemble parts of the human body in colour, shape or qualities. If the juice of a plant resembled any of the four humours – blood, phlegm, black bile or yellow bile – then the plant would cure illnesses relating to those humours.

Healing by astrology was also favoured, but this was mostly the prerogative of the wealthy. It depended on complicated and time-consuming calculations of the positions of the moon and planets. Each planet was believed to govern different parts of the body. Astrology is thought to have originated in Egypt and to have passed thence to Greece and Rome. It was only one of a range of healing methods available to the ancient magician-physicians. They also healed using magical beds, magical rings, stones, and girdles. Of course they also used the horn of the mythical unicorn, or said they did.

Down through the ages, practically everything that grows, plants and animal, even parts of human bodies, everything in the night sky, everything buried in the earth, water, precious stones, ordinary stones, have been invested with extraordinary powers and pressed into the service of healing by these magician-physicians.

One of the most widespread methods – which indeed is still with us – was healing by touch. Sometimes called the 'laying on of hands', it is believed to have originated with the priest-physicians of ancient Egypt. It is probably the most comforting and empathetic of all healing practices, and is the particular gift of two of the people in the chapters that follow. It is still practised as part of their religious duties by Christian priests. Jesus Christ healed by touch: just one instance is the woman with an issue of blood who touched the hem of his garment and was instantly cured.

Healing by touch was practised by monarchs, who were said to receive the power to do so at the anointing with holy oil during their coronations. Even Roman emperor Vespasian, who would hardly have encountered holy oil, was reputed to have healed, albeit unwillingly. England's Queen Elizabeth I touched for scrofula – tuberculosis of the lymph nodes – known in those days as the king's evil. This healing power was seen as confirming the rightful sovereignty of the monarch, so understandably Elizabeth's ministers rejoiced that the gift remained despite England's break with Rome. English monarchs continued intermittently to touch for the king's evil until the death of Queen Anne in 1714.

<hr />

In Ireland, healing is as ancient as the people. It runs right through Irish mythology. There was Dian Ceth, described variously as a druid and as the god of healing – referred to in the *Rosa Anglica* as the Irish Asclepius (the Greek god of healing). The Battle of Moytura, between the Tuatha de Dannan and the Firbolgs, is associated with a memorable feat of healing by Dian Ceth. The story goes that in the course of the battle the king of the Tuatha lost his hand. Dian Ceth stanched the bleeding, dressed the wound, and fitted to the king's wrist a silver hand that was as good as the original. Twenty years later, at the second Battle of Moytura, this time against the Formorians, Dian Ceth was said to have used a bath of herbs to restore the fallen soldiers to life and return them to the battle.

The link between healing and magic is borne out by the fact that professional physicians in ancient Ireland were a branch of the druids. The profession was hereditary, and was for generations retained by the same families. The O'Hickeys were physicians to the O'Briens of Thomond; the O'Shiels ministered to the McMahons. They used an oral tradition of native lore, though their stock-in-trade seems to have been the usual store of contemporary European medicine, such as the *Aphorisms* of Hippocrates, the *Rosa Anglica* of John of Gaddensesden, and the writings of Bernard of Gordon.

Whatever success these physicians may have achieved in looking after their noble patients, there is no doubt of their ability to look after themselves. They had, according to the *Book of Glendalough*, a special seat at the royal banqueting table; the Brehon laws state that a physician was entitled to his own food and food for four apprentices at the house of his patient while the latter was being healed. Physicians were also entitled to wear as many colours as princes of the royal blood, and to wear gold rings.

An eighth-century manuscript attributed to Dian Ceth deals with the level of fees paid for their services. The considerable sums demanded would have ensured that most ordinary people must have lived or died without benefit of the professional physicians. Thus the poorer people had to experiment with herbs and other remedies. Over the centuries their skills developed, and there evolved a corpus of folk remedies, some of which survived right up to present times. Quite a few have been written down and preserved by Lady Wilde, in her *Ancient Legends of Ireland*.[8]

Some of the charms for healing were in the form of a prayer, and many seem as much for emotional as for physical healing:

> A Charm against Sorrow: A charm set by Mary for her Son, before the fair man and the turbulent woman laid him in the grave.

> A Charm to be said by the cross when the night is black and the soul is heavy with sorrow.

> A Charm which God set for Himself when the divinity within Him was darkened.

> A Charm to be said at Sunrise, with hands on the breast, when the eyes are red with weeping, and the madness of grief is strong.

> A Charm that Has no Words, only the silent prayer.

A Charm to Win Love: O Christ by your five wounds, by the nine orders of angels, if this woman is ordained for me, let me hold her hand now, and breathe her breath. O my love, I set a charm to the top of your head; to the sole of your foot; to each side of your breast, that you may not leave me nor forsake me. As a foal after the mare, as a child after the mother, may you follow and stay with me till death comes to part us.

Some of the charms cling to the older ways, to the old druid magic, while making a curtsey towards Christianity. For instance:

A Charm of Most Desperate Love, to be written with a raven's quill in the blood of the ring finger of the left hand: By the power that Christ brought from heaven, mayest thou love me woman! As the sun follows its course, mayest thou follow me. As light to the eye, as bread to the hungry, as joy to the heart, may thy presence be with me, O woman that I love, till death come to part us asunder.

Many such charms suggest a prudent tendency to keep a foot in both camps. A Charm for the Mad Fever recommends the services of 'a wise fairy doctor', and ends with a prayer to the Trinity. The impression is that fairy doctors, people who got their skill or knowledge from the fairies, were an accepted part of life.

Not all the cures recorded by Lady Wilde are merely superstitious: some are quite practical. An example is the Cure for a Burn, which directs the sufferer to take sheep's suet and the rind of an elder tree and boil both together. It was said to cure a burn without leaving a mark. In 1972 the effectiveness of this and similar cures was explained by Dr Patrick Logan: 'The high melting point of the mutton fat is important. If pork fat or beef fat were used, the dressing would soon become a soft mess. The essential points are the quick dressing, the airtight seal, and the fact the dressing must not be disturbed for nine days because the burn would surely become infected when the dressing was changed."

Some of the cures are grotesque, like the Cure for Relief of Toothache:

'Go to a graveyard and kneel upon any grave. Say three Paters and three Aves for the soul for the dead lying beneath. Then take a handful of grass from the grave, chew it well, casting forth each bite without swallowing any portion. After this process the sufferer, were he to live a hundred years, will never have toothache any more.'

Other cures are quite precise and even matter of fact, such as the Cure for Weak Eyes, which states that a concoction of boiled daisy flowers is to be used as a daily eye bath.

While ordinary people used remedies like these, there seem always to have been healers with their own special remedies or powers, people whose lives were dedicated to the curing of other people's ills. Perhaps the best remembered of all in Ireland was Biddy Early, who died on 21 April 1874.

Biddy Early was an extraordinary character by any standard. She should, according to the accepted wisdom of her time, have known her place, and respected her betters (i.e., anyone above her own level of servant girl). Instead she stood up to the establishment, both Church and state, and annoyed both very much.

She was emotionally and professionally committed to the Other World, the world of the Good People, the fairies. She diagnosed most hurts and illnesses as retaliations by the Good People for fairy forts interfered with, or for rubbish thrown on an invisible fairy path. However, the fact remained that if the patient did as ordered by Biddy, he or she recovered.

Scandalised clergy denounced her from the altar, warning people to avoid her, some going as far as to call her a witch. Sheriff and police came to evict her: she could not pay the rent, as she refused to take money for curing people. Her reaction to verbal abuse and attempted eviction was, if not exactly passive, certainly not violent. One priest set out for the Early home with the intention of threatening her and of ordering her out of the area. In a flooded road near the house the priest's horse stopped dead and could not be got to move. Biddy sent word that if the priest promised to let her alone she would free him. He promised, and she did. The tale of the eviction follows the same line — men and beasts unable to move until they agreed to stay away from Biddy Early.

In a book about Biddy Early, Edmund Lenihan quotes an old man who knew her: 'Twas good things she done all the time. Sure, the devil never cured anyone, only made 'em worse if he could. He has nothing to give you, only what he has himself. That's his trade.'

Most of the healers I have come across have two notable things in common with Biddy Early — they are not out to make money, and they constantly do good. In other ways they differ widely from her, as they do from each other. Some stop bleeding by touch; some can cure at a distance; some use herbs; others have secret cures, handed down in a family for generations; some manifest a natural or God-given gift, which seems as inexplicable as water-divining, yet just as real, and usually comes down through a family; some came to healing reluctantly; some do it as a side line; and some devote their lives to it.

No general explanation could embrace all the different healers described here. The only thing we can say for sure is that in a country with such a long and rich tradition of folk healing – ranging from magic to herbs to heredity to faith – it would be surprising if people did not still turn to folk healers when modern medicine fails to help. Or indeed before that.

I have travelled the length of Ireland to meet the healers on these pages, have spent much time with them and with their clients. One other thing I can say for sure: they believe in what they do. They are not charlatans.

In the chapters that follow, I present some of the best known of these healing people of Ireland.

Notes

1. Frederick Thomas Elworthy, *The Evil Eye*, New York, p.24
2. Ibid, p.201
3. S.J.S. Thomson, *Magic and Healing*, New York, p.37
4. Elworthy, *The Evil Eye*, p.49
5. Ibid.
6. John D. St Seymour, *Irish Witchcraft and Demonology*, London, pp.245–6
7. Ibid. p.247
8. Lady Speranza Wilde, *Ancient Legends of Ireland*, London, pp.186–210
9. Patrick Logan, *Irish Country Cures*, Belfast, p.102

❧ *The Stopping of Blood*

LOTIONS, POTIONS, CONCOCTIONS, incantations, water drawn from a secret well when the moon is in the dark quarter, berries plucked from a rowan tree on November Eve – is this the sort of paraphernalia that Brian Keelan uses when he intervenes to stop men and beasts bleeding to death? What can he know, or do, or use, that doctors and vets cannot?

These were the thought I was pondering when I reached Kells, County Meath, on a quest for the man who stops bleeding.

Kells is a small town famous for its treasures from the past, the best known being the *Book of Kells* in Trinity College, Dublin, and the Crozier of Kells in the British Museum in London. Kells can still boast five high crosses, a round tower and the ancient structure called St Columcille's House. Kells was also the setting for one of the most important reforms ever to take place in the Irish Church. Known as the Synod of Kells, in 1152, it suppressed a number of petty bishoprics and instituted four metropolitan provinces: Armagh, Cashel, Dublin and Tuam. These reforms remain to this day.

Kells folk have a quiet satisfaction in the legacy of their cultured past. Brian Keelan is one of them: he is proud of the skill that went into the creation of Kells' great artifacts. He is prouder still, though, of the nearby Hill of Tara, where, according to a long-held tradition, his family has its roots.

I first heard the name Brian Keelan in the waiting-room of one of the other healers in this book. Conversation among the patients had turned to farming and the emergencies that can arise. A woman was telling how a calf had wandered through an open gate and become entangled in barbed wire. 'He was torn asunder,' she said. 'The vet couldn't stop the bleeding.'

Did he die? I asked.

'No,' was the reply. 'We got Brian Keelan.'

At that moment the woman was called into the surgery. I was left with no idea who Brian Keelan was, where he lived, or what he did besides curing bleeding calves, and I wasn't able to wait until the woman came out again.

Six months and dozens of enquiries later, I was now to hear the full story – I hoped.

Until Brian Keelan was fifty years old, he lived a contented and mostly quiet life as a farmer and a water diviner on some of the most fertile land of Ireland, if not of Europe, His home is also the sub-post office in Kells, a traditional meeting place in rural Ireland. He is a cheerful, friendly man, whose easygoing manner reflects that quiet life he used to lead.

Then suddenly Brian Keelan's life shot off in a new and almost frightening direction. In the Keelans' comfortable living-room, among the solid dark furniture, surrounded by family pictures including Brian and Kitty's wedding photographs, I heard the strange story.

'The first time it was a cow jumped a barbed-wire fence, and when I had her in the byre there wasn't a chance of saving her – the blood was running out the door. I put my hand on her and ran to phone the vet. When I was going out the door I looked back and the bleeding had stopped, just like that.'

I examined the face of the man sitting opposite me. He didn't seem like a chancer or a joker: just an ordinary, seemingly decent countryman. He touched, and the bleeding stopped. Or so he said.

Was there a tradition of healing in his family? I asked.

'When I discovered I had all these cures, I got very inquisitive, and began to go back into family history. I often heard my aunts say that our family came from the Hill of Tara in olden times, and had cures in the family. My father wouldn't hear of anything like that, but now maybe I think the aunts were right.'

All these cures? I had thought he only stopped bleeding. What else does he do?

'Well, I do most things. I cure most parts of the body. The principal cures are for migraine and sinus. I never yet failed to cure migraine. I often saw people coming in that door, and they'd be so bad with it they'd just walk into the door; they wouldn't see it. And they were cured. The power is in my hands.'

My mood changed. I felt a sense of lightheartedness, as if there were faraway laughter. I had an impression of gifts bestowed in cheerful generosity, and accepted with a simple joy. A sense of spring, when Brian's years might have indicated autumn.

How did he find out about the other gifts? I asked.

'It was about ten years ago. There was this young lad was down here one night and says I to him, "There's something the matter with you." "Well, there is," he said. "I can't see in front of me with the pain in my head." I went over and put my hands on his head. The pain went like that.' He snapped his fingers.

The efficacy of this healing astonished Brian as much as anyone. I asked him about the other cures.

'I do skin disease too – dermatitis, shingles, ringworm, neuritis, psoriasis – all that sort of thing.' He achieves, he says, one hundred percent success.

Brain haemorrhages are one of the most drastic forms of bleeding: could Brian do anything about them?

'I had one myself, and nearly died, but they whispered in my ear what I had, and the vein sealed itself. They couldn't understand in the hospital how it happened, and they X-rayed me two days running. There were no ill effects from the haemorrhage.'

Although Brian Keelan first began to heal by touching, he no longer has to touch: 'My great-grandfather could stop bleeding, but did it with a prayer. He gave it [the gift] to an aunt of mine, but she never used it. After I began stopping bleeding, she gave me the prayer – about ten years ago – and I always use it now. I never touch now – I don't have to.'

Which is what allowed him to stop a woman from bleeding to death in the United States. Brian was here in Ireland at the time.

'It was a life-and-death case. This lady in Dallas, Texas, had a brain haemorrhage, and had to be operated on. Her brother who lives here told me. I advised him to get me the time of the operation. He came back with the time, and we worked out from American time to Irish time.'

During the operation, the bleeding stopped in a way that no one could explain, at the exact time that Brian had intervened. 'And dammit all, didn't she walk in that door six weeks later, over the operation and doing well.'

That was one of the most preposterous claims of all I had heard in researching this book. I asked to be put in contact with the woman in the US, and this was done through her brother. I wrote her the following letter:

> Dear Ms Newman,
>
> Thank you for your courtesy and help. It means a great deal to me.
>
> Just a few lines saying that you had a brain haemorrhage so many years ago in the US and that during the course of the operation a second haemorrhage occurred. That the surgeon told you afterwards that your complete recovery was a miracle. You later learned that Brian Keelan, in Ireland, who stops bleeding either by direct touch or over a distance, had been asked by your brother to stop your haemorrhage. They, B.K. and your brother, worked out the time the operation would take place.
>
> Thank you again.

This is the woman's written reply:

> Dear Rebecca,
>
> All of the above is true – good luck in your venture
>
> Best wishes, May Newman

Do any of the local doctors avail of Brian Keelan's gift?

'Never. Not at all. It's the friends of the people who are bleeding that bring them to me.'

Perhaps the doctors' attitudes are understandable. After years of training they learn to stop haemorrhage by pressure, tourniquet or coagulant; or to use drugs with familiar properties and predictable effects. Then along comes a man without training, who, people claim, can stop bleeding even across the Atlantic Ocean. To call on him for help, even in emergencies, would be to open the floodgates. It would also be implicitly accepting the possibility of another system of healing which they do not understand, whose source they cannot identify, which does not register on any instrument known to science.

However, neither does Brian Keelan understand the source of his power.

His other healing gifts did not come as easily to Brian as the stopping of blood. He was hesitant, unsure of himself, indeed almost reluctant.

'Someone came to me from County Louth and said to me, "Surely to God if you can stop bleeding, you can cure a pain in the head or anywhere else." Right, I said, strip off, and she did and I treated her by touching. She was as bad with arthritis as you could ever see – she couldn't lift her head. She was perfect afterwards.'

He shows me a letter he received from a County Longford woman, Marie Matthews, who came to him in 1988. She wrote:

> I was struck down with polyanthritis (poly means all). All joints were effected e.g. jawbone, shoulders, elbows, wrists, hands, fingers (not thumbs) hips, knees, ankles, feet, toes and back. There was also 100% bone damage to the hip joint. At that time I was 25 years of age, single and working in Dublin. I was admitted to the Mater Hospital on the 6th May 1988. I was completely disabled, and the only way of being mobile was by wheelchair. I remained in the wheelchair for approximately 6 weeks. I had to be fed, washed, dressed and all other things had to be done for me. With medical care I left the hospital with a walking aid and was

left with no hope of a full recovery. My hands were closed
and feet turning in, I heard about Brian in September '88
and went to his clinic, in the hope of a cure. I attended his
clinic four times. I now have full control over my joints
and am leading a normal life thanks to Brian. I have since
married and I now have three lovely children and I believe
it is all down to Brian Keelan's gift.

Did Brian welcome his new-found healing gift?

"Oh, I did. It's a wonderful thing to see someone
coming in that door not able to lift their arms – you'd
have to help them take off their clothes. And then they'd
go back out walking. That is something.'

Did he improve with practice?

'No. I was as good the first day I got the gift as I am now.
Some people think I might be frightened, but I'm at home
with it. The only thing is, I'm flat out after a day of it. I go
out like a light, even if there is a TV programme I wanted to
see.'

What can Brian Keelan do that conventional medicine
cannot?

'Well, there are no cures for migraine or sinus, or many
of the skin diseases. It's a terrible thing what doctors will do
for these things. Hot baths three times a day for some of
them – I say baths are wrong: you should never wet the
skin, and even rubbing things in is wetting it.

'And then there's arthritis. I put them off hot baths for
that, too. People think these baths will ease them of the
pain. It does for a while, but it comes back worse than
ever.'

When people first started bringing their skin diseases to
Brian Keelan, he would send them to someone else, as he
did not realise he could help them. 'Then one Sunday
evening a woman came here with a child who had a

terrible skin disease. I said, "I don't do it, Ma'am – you'll have to go to someone else." She began to cry, and, sure, I said I'd try to do something. I cured him.'

Brian has had to revamp his life around his healing. The peaceful lifestyle of a well-to-do County Meath farmer was over. Now just about all the time, people seek him out, frightened people, people in pain. As his sensitivity to illness and sorrow increased, his appreciation of his gift grew, and his earlier surprise and joy deepened into commitment.

His commitment has been well tested. 'This young *gasúr* [boy] was brought to me. He was about three years old, and had epilepsy and serious brain damage. A specialist from England had told them the child might live six months if lucky. They came to me three times, and I never heard a word from them again.

'Then one day came a neighbour of theirs. She said to me, "Do you remember so and so?" meaning the little boy. How in the name of God, I said, can I remember four years ago, when I cannot remember who came four days ago? So she reminded me, and I said I took it the child was long dead. "No," she said, "he's as much alive as you or me, and going to school, and is the best scholar in the class."

'That child is seven years old today, and they never let me know. Only for that woman I'd never have known. They should have come back.'

Are many people like that?

'A lot don't come back – that's the sad thing. I only hear from other people how they are doing. Like a carpenter who came to me, in a bad way. A friend of his told me he is now roofing houses on a building scheme. "He couldn't put a foot on a ladder when he came to you," the friend told me.'

Hurt shows in Brian Keelan's face when he speaks about the farming community, in a sense his own people. "Every year I save thousands of pounds worth of cattle with red water, one of those kidney diseases [murrain]. I can get up to twenty calls a day for that, from all over the country. But it's rarely they bother to say thanks.'

The list of illnesses cured after a visit to Brian Keelan includes stomach ulcers, meningitis, even breast cancer. However, there is one area where his powers, if real, are almost scary.

Brian Keelan has been a diviner all his life. That usually means divining water, and I presumed it was so for Brian. Then, casually, he mentioned finding a young man who had been missing for over a year in Peru.

Was the man alive? I asked.

'No,' Brian said. 'I told them he was dead. He was dead beside a lake in Peru.'

Brian uses a diviner's rod when he is searching for water, but in this instance he used a pendulum.

'You have to have a photograph of the person who went missing, to find if he is dead or alive. Then you hold the pendulum over the photograph and you say, is this person dead?'

You *say* it?

'Yes.'

You actually *ask* the pendulum?

'Yes.'

Who are you asking?

Brian: 'You actually say, "Is this person dead?" And if he is, the device will come clockwise in your hand. If he is not dead, it will come the other way. So who am I asking? The Man Above, I suppose!'

You said, 'I suppose.' How can you be sure it's the Man Above?

Brian gets a little sore. 'Well, there's the powers I have for divining, you know.'

But where do you think those powers come from?

'It's the Man Above. Only for him, none of us would be here. That's my belief.'

You said that some powers came through your ancestors, the earliest of whom would have been pagan, and at the same time you are saying, the Man Above. Are you actually narrowing it down to God, or not?

Brian: 'Where does anything come from?'

Where indeed? But have you thought through where exactly this power comes from? I'll put it another way — do you ask an unknown source?

'Yes.'

As far as you are concerned, you are addressing an unknown source. You hope it is God, but you don't know. You cannot be one hundred per cent sure that what you are addressing is God. All you know is a pendulum.

Brian: 'An unknown source, that's right. But it's the same in water divining — if you find a spring, the thing turns down in your hand. You have come on the spring.'

That could be a different thing altogether. You are talking about a power in yourself that might respond to elements, minerals or something else in the ground. That's not the same as asking a pendulum about something that is happening or has happened thousands of miles away, and has no connection with your locality.

What source are you addressing, Brian Keelan? To what power do you speak, when you ask the pendulum? In fact you are not really asking the pendulum — you are using it as a go-between, like a telephone. So here we go again. *What source of power are you addressing?*

Brian: 'I never thought about it at all, except that it was God. I never really questioned.'

🌱 *The Woman with the Bottle*

'I S IT THE woman with the bottle you want?'
The man, who had got off his bicycle when I hailed him from my car to enquire where I could find May Dempsey, looked at me with the friendly interest of a country person who never seems too busy to pass the time of day. He sported a check tweed cap, the kind that goes to the races and looks well even after years of wear. Sporty or not, he was a careful man, and took no chances that I might find myself in the wrong place.

'You mean the woman with the cure?'

The very same, I said. The woman with the cure, the woman with the bottle, was the woman I had come to Portarlington to visit. Following his detailed directions, correct even to the colour of the gates I would pass, I found the Dempsey farm.

Mrs May Dempsey, a welcoming, warm, humorous woman of middle years, cures brucellosis, known to her in her youth as the *minaireach*, as her family have done for some one hundred years. They have never charged for what they do.

'Well, with us the cure was given to my mother on condition that she never took any money. I continued that. I never charge. People do leave gifts, but no money what-soever. People have left money, but, unless I cannot get in touch with them, I do not keep it, not even the price of a phone call. I return it if I can.'

May Dempsey did not welcome her gift. 'Something over twenty years ago, when Mother had a heart attack, she grew very anxious to leave the cure with me. She said she was giving it to me, just in case. The way she gave it was, she gave me the prayer to say and the name of the sick person. That was all there was with her. Except of course the bottle.'

Apparently the cure involves a certain herb which, when rubbed in May Dempsey's hand, can indicate if the person has brucellosis, simply by the way it reacts. The same herb, mixed in water and bottled, can then cure the disease. May does not say what herb it is.

'It is a herb that grows wild and it is not easily got,' she says, 'although, now, thanks be to God, over the years we are finding more places where it grows. I run it under cold water to take all the clay out of it, and then I rub and rub it and use it with cold water. It's all cold.

'I wasn't anxious to take over the cure, because I had spent all my youth picking herbs for other people. So I didn't wel-come the gift at all. I was disgusted with it. I thought, oh no, not again! I'm still going to be saddled with this. But I never thought of saying no. There was no question on my part of not taking the cure. All my mother's life, she said, "Well, when you have this", or "When you'll be making this", and it went on that way. I just accepted it. I suppose it was being brought up in stricter times. But I hadn't any great faith in myself when I started.'

Although in fact her mother recovered and lived for another twenty years, May carried on curing from the moment she got the gift. She is determined that she will pass on the gift to one of her children – she has three teenagers – but her way of doing it will be different. She will explain to them what to do, and leave it up to any one of them who wants to do it. She will not force it on any of them.

We left the future to take care of itself and got back to the beginning of Mrs Dempsey's healing experiences.

'The first man that came to me when I started was this man who had brucellosis, and had been in Cherry Orchard Hospital for six weeks. At that time, if you had fever, it was high fever, and that was that. He was very, very ill. So I tried the Cure on him, and he got better. Completely cured. He was grand.

'Then another fellow brought the bottle to America with him. He was a footballer, and he was going to play a match, but he had brucellosis. It seems he was a very good footballer, and he did play the match.' Casually she added, 'I didn't know him myself, personally, at all.'

I must have got it wrong, I thought. How could May Dempsey diagnose that a man, whom she had never seen, had brucellosis?

I had, it seemed, heard correctly.

'Now, what I'm going to tell you is very hard to understand. This is the part that has to be the gift. I can tell if the person complaining has brucellosis or not, even if that person is not here. The way I'm able to tell is, that when I rub the herb in a certain way, it makes up. If the person has brucellosis, it will go into a blacky-white foam. If the person has not got it, the herb stays the way it is, and green water, literally green water, will come out of it. I could not explain how it happens.

'When some people come here, maybe they might think, how the heck can she say whether it's brucellosis or not. But if they do have it, and when they begin to feel better, they accept it.'

May appears to take such things in her stride.

'I've cured people in America, Australia, all over the world, and I've never met them, never seen them, nor ever will. I know there is one I will never meet on this earth anyway, because he died since. His brother was here with me, and he brought the bottles to Shannon. The man had a heart problem as well – that's what killed him. But he got good health for years after getting cured from the brucellosis. He got on great.'

She knows little of the origins of the gift. Her mother got it from her aunt-in-law, and her mother would be eighty now, if she had lived. May Dempsey was never interested in how her cure originated until years later, when her mother was not able to tell her.

'Growing up with the cure in the house,' she says, 'I never questioned anything. I looked at it all as everyday things. You see, I didn't know anything different.'

Yet strange things happen when that herb is placed in her hand and rubbed. For instance, it reacts strongly if handled with a gloved hand. Describing the antics of the herb, Mrs Dempsey was inclined to laugh, in the half-amused, half-resigned way people have when they describe the goings-on of a mischievous pet.

'Sometimes my hands are black from rubbing the herb. I tried rubber gloves once, but it was no good. The herb wouldn't stay in my hands. It went over my shoulder and out the window, and everywhere. I suffer notoriously from my hands, from the rubbing. I get pains, and my hands open, and cracks come in them. But when I put on these – nurse's theatre gloves they were – I was saying, oh, this is great, this is great, and I was trying to rub. The next thing, the herb went into a ball and — whew, it flew over my shoulder. I got it back and I tried again, and it scooted out through that window. It would not stay in my hands.'

The gift also seems to have a mind of its own:

'After my mother giving me the cure, a brother of mine got brucellosis. Now at that time I was in bed, very ill and covered with bandages. A pressure cooker had exploded all over me, and I was badly burned. So Mother said to my brother, sure I'll make it while May is sick. But it wouldn't work for her. Once she had given the gift away, it was gone from her.'

Although May Dempsey was a reluctant conscript in the healer's army, today the cure is a very important part of her life.

'I feel great about it now. I get great satisfaction. I suppose it has brought us great happiness, in one way or another. If there was only one person you have helped, it would be great. In my case now, I suppose it has gone into thousands.

'I'm over twenty years at it, and there's great happiness in the family, for though my kids are teenagers, there is no squabbling going on in the house. For the one reason: nobody has time. Well, literally, you come in, and there is always a stranger in the house.'

While we talked the telephone rang and May went to answer it. I thought about her. She has had three children, three pregnancies, sick babies, wakeful nights. Today she has all the daily needs of the family to see to, meals to prepare, the gathering of the herb for the cure and the very hard work of the cure itself. The actual rubbing of the herb and making the medicine takes a lot out of her. 'Many a night when I'd have a big crowd, I wouldn't be able to lift my arms, and my shoulders would be very sore. You must be prepared to put a lot of yourself into it.'

She is available every day of the week to all who call. Patients are ushered into the parlour or the kitchen. I wondered if her family minded having strangers around all the time. It would hardly be surprising if they got tired of it. 'They don't really mind. Sometimes they might say, Oh Lord, not somebody else. But once, after a spell of bad weather, when nobody came for weeks on account of the frost and snow, one of the lads said, "I wish to God somebody would come for a bottle. It's the loneliest house ever." So you see they don't really know what loneliness is.'

Mrs Dempsey's husband, John, seems to cope well with the disruption that the cure brings to family life. A man with a heavy day's work behind him, hungry and maybe wet through, as a farmer might be, could hardly be always in the humour for the company of strangers. Yet 'I suppose, he's the happiest type of man in the world. He has to be, or he'd go mad. An odd time he might say, if he was very tired, "Oh Lord, not again", but it's rarely he'd mind. And he loves meeting people.'

Much of the joy in May's life derives from the people met and the friendships made – and of course the cures achieved. There was the woman who could not walk and now goes everywhere on her bike, and the girl who first came in a wheelchair, and took over a year to get better. There was the model from England, who had been told she would be in a wheelchair in six months, and had no hope. 'She is flying today,' Mrs Dempsey says gratefully.

Doctors react to Mrs Dempsey's cure in a number of different ways. Some reject it out of hand; some are coming to terms with it.

'Quite a lot are letting my name slip,' May says. 'They put it into the mouths of people by saying, "If you're up around Portarlington, there's a woman there who claims

she can cure brucellosis." Now that could be putting people on the right lines, or it could be sarcasm. They cannot
say to a patient, "Look here, go out to Mrs Dempsey."
Then again, there are doctors who go down people's
throats if they said they were with me.'

May Dempsey's cure is not easy to take. Even when
people are diagnosed as having brucellosis, and the cure has
started, their troubles are in a sense only beginning. 'My
bottle starts by making people worse for a long time.' The
patient drinks the medicine once a day, and at first it may
induce nausea or headaches, occasionally a rash. 'It's tough
on anyone that takes it. It gives a lot of pains and aches, and
sickness, but it is worth it.

'Another thing. If after starting my cure, they drink whiskey, then I'm bet! If they drink whiskey before they come, I
can cure them. But if they go back on it, I'm beaten. And in
my opinion, any cure that doesn't continue is not a cure.'

People who will not take money for a service are rare. I
put it to May that there might be circumstances in which
she could change her mind about accepting money. She
repeated, even more firmly, if that were possible, 'NO, NO.
No money whatsoever. There are people, healers, who have
to buy stuff. But I don't. I use nothing that costs money. Do
you understand me? So I think, in my case, it would be
badly abusing the gift if I were to charge or take money.'

There is a price, of course, but the price is paid by May
herself. Occasionally, a terrible sadness and a feeling of
helplessness comes over her when she meets a patient
who has been to doctor after doctor and sees her as a last
hope, and she has to tell them that their disease is not
brucellosis, and thus she cannot be of any help either.

Gift healers appear compelled to help people. All of those
I visited share their gifts and their time. Some share their

homes. But May Dempsey and one or two others go beyond this, and share their lives.

I left May Dempsey, my mind puzzling over unresolved questions, her brucellosis cure a mystery. When May first spoke about it, I presumed that somebody in the long ago had stumbled on a herb that cured brucellosis. Later, when she told me about the strange behaviour of the herb, my theory fell apart, and questions sprouted everywhere. Consider some of them.

With every patient a test is made, using the herb that is a central part of the cure. If the test is positive, showing that brucellosis is present, the already partly processed herb is put into water and the cure made up – no waste of time, material or energy.

But how did the system for the curing of brucellosis develop?

May Dempsey does not know. Her lack of curiosity about her gift – a trait she, curiously, seems to share with many other healers – means that she never asked.

And how does a weed curl into a hard ball and then jump twice, once through a window.

How can a *weed* connect two human beings, even though they may be thousands of miles apart, enabling, or even forcing, the brucellosis to identify itself?

How did May Dempsey's mother lose the gift the moment she gave it to her daughter? When she tried to cure her son, she was clearly under the impression that she was now sharing her gift with her daughter. So has the gift a built-in power to accept the resignation, even the unintended resignation, of the incumbent healer, and relieve him or her of all duties?

Why may only one person, or at any rate, one member of a family, practise the gift at the one time?

Why must May Dempsey herself give the herb? Some of her patients have tried gathering the same herb, yet it doesn't work for them. They have told her they might as well be drinking water.

Is the healer the most important element in the cure? Or is the herb of equal value? Would any herb do?

It is as if the whole thing had been devised, arranged, and programmed. But by whom or what? The questions pile up. Every what raises a why, and every why raises a how, and every how raises . . .

Or maybe it is all blind chance. Maybe there is neither plan nor purpose. Maybe the herb and the healer just came together by accident. Maybe.

🔥 *The Mystery of the Burn Oil*

I F YOU HEARD about a cure for burns and your experience of burns was limited to the occasional brush with a hot iron or an overfull teapot, you might agree that it sounded very interesting and let it slip from your mind. However, if you were unfortunate enough to have a two-quart kettle of boiling water spill over you, burning you from waist to ankle, or have a car radiator spray its boiling contents on to your face and arms and chest, if you were in dreadful pain and your doctors could do very little to help you, a cure for burns would clearly become very important.

I first heard about the cure from Rosaleen, a woman who had a kettle of boiling water overturn and burn her stomach and legs.

'It was the day Cecilia made her First Communion,' she told me. 'Everything was a mad rush, with two smaller children in the way. Well, you can imagine! Anyway, wasn't I passing the cooker, passing myself out nearly, when the cloth I was carrying caught the kettle and down it came, right over me. To make bad worse, the lid fell off and it was like a fountain, just like a scalding fountain.

'Well, my husband Jim is a great friend of Mrs Boyle, and hadn't she given him a bottle of the burn oil a few weeks before it happened. She just gave him the stuff as a present for old times' sake, you know.'

I didn't know. I tried to halt Rosaleen, to find out who Mrs Boyle is, and what this 'burn oil' is. I don't think she even heard me, and I watched my chance to insert the questions between the heel of one word and the toe of the next, as they skidded excitedly out of her mouth. I found out that the woman with the cure for burns is a Mrs Boyle, who lives near Dunmore in County Galway, and that she makes up a burn oil which has been in her family since 'her mother's grandmother's time'.

Were you long in the hospital? I asked my informant.

Rosaleen's face took on a look of resigned patience. 'I wasn't in hospital. I went to the First Communion.'

Oh, then the water wasn't quite boiling? Just hot. Still, that was bad enough.

'I told you, it was boiling. That was why I was rushing. The kitchen was filled with steam. Jim put on the burn oil straight away, and we lathered it in about every half-hour or so. It happened about 10 o'clock in the morning, and the Communion wasn't till 3 o'clock.'

I didn't think that Rosaleen was telling lies just to make a good story better. Still it was hard to accept that a woman who had had a kettle full of boiling water cascade over her would have been able to go out five hours later without shock, pain or mark.

She looked at me with a mixture of amusement and irritation, knowing well what I was thinking. 'I know it is hard to believe, but I'll tell you what – do you know where Logstrup is?'

I do, I said.

'Well, go out there, and ask for Robert Power, and see what he thinks of Mrs Boyle and her burn oil.'

It would be hard to imagine anybody less likely than Robert Power to opt for a traditional cure rather than high-tech modern hospital treatment. He is a young, skilled, highly qualified production manager in a company that manufactures electrical goods.

In the summer of 1981, Robert Power was travelling from Waterford with his fiancée, who is from Dunmore in County Galway. Outside Limerick city the car over-heated. 'Foolishly I took off the radiator cap. The whole lot of the boiling water sprayed right on to my face, chest, arms and all the way down my left side.'

A man in a nearby garage drove him to Barrington's Hospital. 'I was in shock. They gave me a prescription for some ointment. I think I got there too soon, and the blisters had not come out.'

He was back in Dunmore before any blisters appeared, though they had to stop on the way for painkillers. 'The pain was something terrific,' Robert remembers. The doctor in Dunmore gave him a prescription for more ointment, and later, when the pain got worse, decided to send him to hospital.

'That was about three days after the accident. I was in an awful lot of pain. I couldn't sleep, or anything.

'Then my girlfriend, now my wife, mentioned Mrs Boyle, and, instead of going to hospital, we went to see her. She said the burns were too bad, and she would be nervous to try anything, but when we asked her the second time, she said she would try.

'The first thing she did was to burst all the blisters with a sterilised needle. Then she took this special oil, and she put on some gauze, and then she painted the oil on over the gauze with feathers. I actually got a night's sleep that night, for the first time since the burning.'

How did the doctor react when you told him that you had changed your mind about going to hospital?

'Well, I went back to him, and I told him I was going to the lady. He didn't object, or say anything to disagree. He did say that Mrs Boyle had cured a lot of people.

'I had to go back to her every night for a week. Then she gave me the oil and feathers, so that I could do the dressings myself. She didn't cover my face at all, though there were a lot of blisters and broken skin and that type of thing. It came perfect.'

⁂

Agnes Boyle is a friendly, cheerful, woman, quite elderly now and with grey hair, though she looks healthy, hardy. She has a wonderfully mobile and expressive face. When she is speaking about badly burnt people – especially small children – sympathy and understanding of the horrors of burning can be read in her gestures and expression.

She lives in a two-storey farmhouse with a sloping garden bright with flowers. Inside it is warm and comfortable. The kettle is on the boil, and there is the tempting smell of baking bread.

She remembered Robert Power.

'To tell you the truth, I was nearly running a mile from him. He was in a terrible mess altogether – his face and chest and arms. His face and glands and everything were all swelled up. I asked him would he do as I told him if I took him on, and he said, anything you ask, I will do.

'I told him, you must go to someone – Robert was not a native of Dunmore and had no family here – and you must lie down and be dressed. You can get up and put the stuff on your face yourself, because I won't be covering your face.

'So he had the oil in a saucer, covered with another saucer, and I gave him the feathers. He was able to do his own face. His face was all right in four or five days.'

In order to apply the oil to his body Mrs Boyle made up a garment which covered Robert from head to toe.

'What I had to do for Robert was like making a vestment for a priest. I got a big piece of gauze. His mother-in-law (she wasn't his mother-in-law then), who was a dressmaker, had to cut a hole for the head. You put the oil outside the gauze, and then bandage over that. It was a sort of shift made from the gauze. He was all right in three weeks.'

It would be wonderful if all Mrs Boyle's experiences were as happy as that one, but there are also the if-onlys, the regrets. Not quite grief, but echoes of grief.

There was the child who fell into the coal fire.

'The child's face and two hands! These two fingers' – pointing to the two first fingers on her left hand – 'and the fingers on the other hand had all gone stiff. The face of the child was tragic. Tragic.

'He was going to a Dublin hospital, and they had stuck something like suede on his head, with holes for his nose and eyes. And do you know that sticky thing you put on sandals – that was on the back of the suede. It was to keep the face from crimpling, and he was to wear if for two years.

'The mother wrote to me, and I took up my pen immediately and I wrote back to her that I could do nothing at that stage. But I said that if she wanted to know anything, to come to me. The woman came, and brought the child.

'I wouldn't think he will ever get over it. His hands . . .
And do you know, they were trying to bring him to a
physiotherapist for his hands. And he was so frightened that
he used to work into fits. And so they stopped. And that
means that his hands are like this' – she turned her fingers
inwards – 'when you straighten them, they go back again.

'He's an only child, and he was born perfect,' she added.

This is probably the saddest might-have-been in Mrs
Boyle's healing life. 'I'd have had that child right in two
weeks,' she said. 'I'm telling you about that oil: in all fairness
it is the greatest thing that was ever made for burns. Because
you have no mark, no stiffness, there is no physiotherapy
needed, no need to put your arm in a sling, or anything like
that. Nothing needed after it.'

I felt it might sometimes be hard to look at burns and
to touch them. Did you ever feel revolted? I asked her.

Earlier she had said that bad burns, especially burns four
or five days old, can be very messy, all blood and everything, and have to be cleaned off first. But she never felt
nauseated. It's a part of her life.

'My whole ambition was to train as a nurse, but they
wanted me at home. Looking back I'm as far on as the ones
that went. I got married and I was, thank God, happy. We
worked hard, but we had great peace and happiness.'

Did the gift of curing bring you happiness?

'Yes, it did. You have no idea of the joy and happiness
you get in curing all those burnt people, like the ten-day-
old baby, and the nurse, and hundreds of others. That is
why I'm so sorry I can't get the base for the oil.'

The oil which is the basis of Mrs Boyle's cure cannot be
got now. This is causing her great difficulty. Sanctuary oil, if
she could get the real thing, would do. She got some from
the Augustinians in Ballyhaunis and it worked perfectly, but

it is no longer available. She has a tin of oil she got from Germany, but it proved to be of no use. She has new oil now, that came from America, and she is hoping that it will be all right.

There is a sense of urgency in Mrs Boyle's voice when she speaks about the difficulty of getting oil. She feels it would be a calamity if anybody badly burnt were to come to her and she were unable to help.

There are children who might have been disfigured except for Mrs Boyle's burn cure. A woman from a nearby town, who was carrying a pressure cooker, stumbled over her child. The water went over the child's head and face.

'You can imagine that in a two-year-old child. The doctor had her on morphine, on all kinds of things to ease her down. I was afraid the child would die, she was that bad. The child was five days burnt when I saw her, and was roaring day and night. The parents didn't sleep since she was burnt. They had to carry her round and round in their arms the whole time.

'They brought her into me wrapped in a sheet and a blanket. The way it was, I just wanted to give her ease, so I opened her up and I put the oil on, and I told them not to come back the next day, as she needed the rest. But I gave them oil.

'The next time I saw them, I remember well the father coming in that door saying the child had slept for five and a half hours. I had to cut all the hair off. The stuff the hospital had sprayed on had gone like rubber on the outside. It was terrible. Terrible.

'I remember that Christmas. I didn't enjoy it: I thought the child would die.

'I will say this, and I'm not saying anything but God's honest truth: that child was brought from death to life.

She was so badly burnt that I could not see her surviving the pain, shock, the misery. The oil takes away the pain and cools them down.

'The doctor was delighted, and why wouldn't he?'

Mrs Boyle charges a small token fee for the oil. However, she has given oil 'to umpteen people that couldn't afford it. But I take great joy . . . There were young people that were starting off in life, completely cured, not a mark on them.'

People generally appreciate what Agnes Boyle has done for them. When her husband, Jack, died some years ago, she got hundreds of messages and Mass cards. 'I'd have to be trying to think who they were, and who they weren't,' she says now.

Sometimes, of course, people who come to her behave insensitively, and it hurts, but her lively sense of humour overcomes her natural indignation. 'I've often cured people,' she says, 'and they'd go back again to the doctor and never say they were with me. Never say a thing. One, a nurse, even asked me not to tell anybody that I had cured her. She was nearly afraid to say it in the hospital.'

One of her happiest memories is of an old man: 'There was an old maneen, a typical bachelor who has a lot and has nothing. He fell asleep by the fire, and didn't the wellington boot burn into his leg. It was terrible . . . the rubber, y'see. He used to come here, and we had such fun. And he was so thankful, so appreciative that I took him out of such pain.'

Margaret Finnigan of Dunmore, County Galway, expressed similar appreciation in a letter to the author. 'Two years ago,' she wrote, 'my father Joe Mullin, Derreen, Kilkerrin, Ballinasloe was washing the milking machine with boiling water. The water spilt and burnt his foot very badly. He attended Agnes Boyle who healed the burn with cream.

He did not need any phisiotherapy and did not have any scar from the burn.'

<hr/>

We are drawing towards the end of our interview and while we have spoken about many things, still there is a lot left unsaid. Mrs Boyle does not mention the nights she stayed at home because some burnt person had to come back to her. She never talks about things she wanted to to do, but didn't because somebody needed her. Nor does she complain about the times she had to leave her house to look after itself, while she went to people who needed her help.

So far, none of her family have shown any interest in the cure, but she hopes that one of them will carry on. 'Because when you think of the great things that oil did . . . For instance, I saw pictures of that North Sea oil thing on the BBC, and whatever plastic surgery they do, these men will never come back to normal. But I saw worse coming in that door, and now they have no marks whatever.'

Most of the gift healers I visited believe that if others knew the ingredients and the method, they could also achieve the same cures. They regard the recipe as a trust to be kept secret, and handed on within the family if possible.

Mrs Boyle thinks differently. 'My honest opinion is that it would not work for anybody else. At least I don't think so.

'When the children were small, they got an awful dose of ringworm. They went to doctors and chemists, and we were putting on this and that. Somebody said to me, why don't you go to Mr Conneally – he's another healer that does ringworm. So I went, and brought the kids; and he just made the sign of the cross and blew on them three times, and the thing disappeared. Isn't it a hard thing to understand, that a worm would die by your hand? It is just a mystery.'

A man whose gift is in his hands said to me, 'I follow pain.' Mrs Boyle does not follow pain. She prepares for it, and waits for it, contests with it and, whether it is an eighty-year-old man or a ten-day-old child, she has always defeated it.

'Nobody ever died, thank God. Nobody ever came back to me for a thing. Never. I healed anybody I ever put a hand on.'

❦ The Circulation Man

JIMMY CONROY IS a big man with a quiet confident manner. He lives with his wife and five children in the village of Drim, outside Mountrath in County Laois. Powered by enormous energy and commitment, he uses his healing gifts quite independently of technology or drug-based modern medicine.

Conroy is a circulationist. Indeed, he is *the* circulationist because, as far as he can discover, he is the only one in Europe practicing this technique of healing. However, he has recently had tidings of a Scandinavian doctor who has been thinking 'along the same lines as myself', and who is soon to publish the results of his research. Other European doctors tell him that his methods and ideas are simply not part of orthodox medicine.

The key to Jimmy Conroy's healing is manipulation of the circulatory system. He believes that the circulation of blood in the body has a vital role in health and healing, and has too long been neglected in conventional medicine. Jimmy began to study and eventually master techniques of manipulating the body's natural circulation, and can in this way, he says, cure ninety per cent of the ailments brought to his attention.

This rather extravagant-sounding claim is endorsed in striking fashion by the people who, week in and week out, on Mondays and Wednesdays – his two open days – take their place outside the Conroy home, from one o'clock in the morning onwards. Other days are by appointment only, and these are always booked for four to five months ahead. Owners of vans sometimes put mattresses on the floors, and pass the night waiting in some kind of comfort. People bring food, because they know they may be waiting much of the next day.

Jimmy Conroy's story could be called an adventure into healing. Healing is traditional in the Conroy family. 'All my ancestors used to treat and make up their own cures for animals. But I got completely away from the animals: it would be impossible to cure both Christians and animals.'

Like many teenagers, Jimmy Conroy loved to play sport, especially football, but early on he realised that his gift was in his hands rather than in his feet. When he was about seventeen or eighteen, and already interested in first aid because of his sporting involvements, he realised that 'anybody that got an injury, I could find it when I examined him'.

A young mother, paralysed after a stroke, was the first person Jimmy Conroy ever healed. After three sessions of deep manipulation, she could walk. His second cure was of the victim of a serious circulatory problem affecting the kidneys. The muscles at the back had closed in and blocked an artery.

So began the journey to what is a new concept in healing, one that must be lonely at times, even for so determined and independent-minded a man as Jimmy Conroy.

From the first, he was drawn to massage. 'I studied the Roman and Chinese methods, and they did cure people by manipulation. They were on the right track, but they did it the wrong way. I found with most masseurs that they massage up the body. The muscles run down the body, not up. I manipulate from the heart, from the brain, the first part of the body to be formed. Then, if I meet a clot I can dissolve it so it won't get away from me and go back to the heart. If the fluid goes hard in the body, I can crush the fluid back into liquid, so there is no problem to the body. That is why it is all so safe.'

There are three fluids coming from the brain – blood, servo senosis and lymphatic fluid. Each has a different function and each one, when it goes wrong by blockage, clots or crystallisation, can cause discomfort, illness or death.

When Jimmy Conroy realised that he had a gift, he started to work with old people in the district. Some he massaged up, and some down the body. 'One of my first patients was a man of eighty-one years, who could not get out of the chair without help. After two sessions he was riding a push bike. When I say he was riding, he could ride the bike for ten miles. And he started to walk again at that age. It was then I knew my theory worked. I had massaged him down the body.'

Gradually more and more people began to come to Jimmy Conroy, and he worked on them at night after work. His work load got bigger and bigger. Finally in 1974 he made the decision to devote himself to healing and give up his job: 'I had a very good job with Bord na Móna. It was a difficult decision to give up the job and take up healing full time, so as to help people.'

There is little formality in the waiting-rooms of any of the traditional healers I visited, and Jimmy Conroy's waiting-room is no exception. There are few of the usual things we associate with doctors' waiting-rooms - no antismoking poster, no receptionist in a white coat, no *Readers Digests* or dog-eared medical journals. There are, as in any healer's waiting room, people, lots of them, talking freely about their illnesses. A woman from County Mayo told us that for over two years she had not had a full night's sleep unless she was, as she described it, 'doped to the last'.

'I got shingles about two years ago,' she told us, 'and it didn't seem to respond to the medicine the doctor gave me. Then the whole thing went to my head, and oh God, the pain. I finished up in the hospital, but got no better. Then I was given an injection into the part of my face where the pain was worst, and I really thought I would go mad. I never knew there could be such pain.'

A friend heard about Jimmy Conroy and told her, and just a fortnight previously she had come to Drim for the first time. That night there had been some relief. The next night she had slept, waking only now and then.

She had to wait a fortnight before Jimmy would do any more manipulation, because, as he explained to her, he had to 'give the body time to heal. I heal within the body.' She told us that she would camp out happily on the roadside, if it were necessary, to get to Jimmy Conroy.

Others in the waiting-room joined in. A pretty woman in her twenties told us that her legs retained abnormal amounts of fluid, and that her last effort to do something about it had cost £90 for a vein-scan plus the advice that she would have to learn to cope, as she would have to live with it.

'I could live with it,' she said. 'I had not much choice. But cope with it, come to accept it? That I couldn't.'

She had heard that there was somebody who might be able to help her, and after a session of manipulation with Jimmy Conroy she had three weeks of seeing her legs 'looking just like anybody else's'. By the time we saw her, the legs had filled up again. 'But I know now it can be treated and cured,' she told us cheerfully, 'so I don't care if I have to come every month for years.'

An old man called Michael showed us his legs. 'Black as coal they were,' he said, as he rolled up his trousers. Now the legs were a healthy pink.

'I used never bother about them,' Michael remembered. 'Even though the legs were always cold and turning black, I thought it was just age. "Who'd be looking at your legs, anyhow!" herself used to say, laughing at me, y'know.'

Then a neighbour, whose feet were similarly cold and also growing black, had a leg removed. It had been gangrene.

All the fun stopped. Michael's fears grew as black as his legs. 'But my son – he's inside there now in the room – he got a bit of a jerk in the back, and he heard of Jimmy Conroy and went to him. Well, thank God he did, because it brought me to him.' And he pulled up the trouser legs again to admire his grand pink legs.

Gangrene, that creeping terror, was uppermost in my mind when I met with Jimmy Conroy after the last of the patients had gone.

What can the doctors do? I asked. What do they do about gangrene?

'At the start I asked a lot of doctors what they say to patients who have a serious circulation problem. Well, in fact they say very little, because they cannot correct it. They have no treatment for it.

'A good number of doctors who send patients with phlebitis [an inflammation of veins] to me will not allow them to walk until they come here first. If I get patients in time, I can save legs and feet. There are a lot of people who have legs and toes amputated, and there is no need for it.'

I searched for a tactful way to suggest that he might save a great deal of suffering and premature death by sharing his knowledge and skills. Before I could say it he continued:

'Doctors understand when I explain to them, but they cannot put it into practice. They have not been trained to use their hands. They have not got the touch. My biggest problem is that I find it impossible to train people.'

He went on: 'I was born with a gift in my hands. When I examine a person, I can tell exactly what is wrong. I know it through the nervous system and through all the systems in the body. If I examine a person's muscles I know if the muscles are knotted, and whether the fluids are flowing. And I can find any damaged cells in the muscles.'

But how do you know? I asked. Do you know how you know?

'I just know. It is a gift, and it is through the nervous system — a sense of touch. That is how I know.'

How many conditions can this gift-touch reveal, I wondered — conditions usually only discovered through X-rays or scans?

'If you have the feeling, you can go over a person's body and find and identify a trapped nerve, and then you can go and release the nerve. That is easily enough done.'

A little tartly, I said, If it is so easy, why can't doctors do it?

'Because, as I told you, they never worked with their hands.

'I had a patient with a very bad back. He had an operation and had a trapped nerve. I released the nerve but I told him that the pain would come back in four or five days and be every bit as bad. There was a growth of tissue between one disc and the next. I told him to go to the surgeon and have another operation, because I couldn't get in near the tissue.

'The man went back to the surgeon and rang me later to say that the surgeon had told him there was no tissue. I told him to get a second opinion. He did, and the second surgeon operated and removed the tissue. That man is walking perfectly today because later I was able to build up the muscles and tendons and rebuild his back.

'The only person with a bad back that I can do nothing for is a person with a leaking disc. If a disc is leaking there is nothing I can do. It has to be the medical people. The important thing is never to take chances with the body.'

One of Jimmy Conroy's former patients, from Portlaoise, County Laois, offers this account of the effectiveness of Jimmy's technique:

> It started roughly twenty years ago, while lifting a cable drum carrier I wrenched my back. The pain went away after four or five days and it came back from time to time for three to six days. This continued for four or five years and then became more frequent and the pain got worse.
>
> I attended bonesetters all over the country – the best relief I got was from a bonesetter in Kiskeame in Cork. However, as my back got worse if I drove over a pothole while in the car I was in trouble again. I reached a stage when I could no longer work. Up until this point I would have good and bad days.   It was what I was doing on the days I was good that did all the harm.
>
> My doctor recommended I see a specialist, so I visited Mr Martin Walsh an Orthopaedic Surgeon in the Mater Hospital. At this stage my back and right leg was at its worst. I needed crutches to walk around. After Mr Martin Walsh's assessment he confirmed to me that my back was "in a serious state". After waiting three month I then had a myelogram. Results were two enlarged discs between the 3rd, 4th, 5th and 6th vertebrae in the lower lumbar area of my back. Now on a waiting list for surgery.

During this waiting period I heard about Jimmy Conroy
– so I went to Jimmy. Jimmy said he would have me back
training in a month's time as he knew I played hurling with
a local club in Laois. At this stage I would have settled for
being able to stand up straight again. However, I visited
Jimmy twice a week for two to three weeks – a little
improvement. Six weeks later I woke up with no pain.
Before this I was taking pain killers every few hours to keep
the pain away so that I could get a few hours sleep. During
this time the most sleep I got was two hours per night.

Six weeks later the pain was gone. I informed Mr Walsh
that I would not be needing an operation – he asked me to
call and see him. He said I "was extremely lucky and that I
did not need surgery" – he asked me who I attended and
what he did – he said he "still believes in miracles".

I had been unable to work for almost six months. I did
play a few hurling matches just to prove I could. I still play
golf and Badminton at a competitive level.

Thanks to Jimmy Conroy.

Jimmy Conroy has very strong views on people with
nervous problems. His views might not win much applause
from psychiatrists because he says that 'from my experience I
believe that only about twenty per cent of people who are in
mental hospitals belong there. Nine out of ten people that
comes to me have a problem with their nervous system,
because if you have a muscle, a ligament or a tendon problem, the nerves are trapped.

'I cannot come to terms with people with nervous problems being put on medication or tranquillisers. That is
completely wrong. A large number of patients who are in
mental hospitals for maybe three or four months every year
could be taken off all medication after two sessions of

manipulation. It is only with massaging or deep manipulation that a nervous problem can be solved.'

We moved to enemy country, to the hard-core killers – the heart attacks, cancers, strokes.

Jimmy Conroy cannot cure heart attacks, but he can help prevent them. 'I can only treat the muscles on the outside of the body. I cannot get into the internal ones. But I can at least improve the circulation of the blood so that it won't thicken.' And he can, as said earlier, dissolve clots so that they do not return to the heart.

Cancer? 'It depends on where the disease is. Cancer is caused by crystallisation of the lymphatic fluids. If it is on the outer part of the body I can break down the crystals and get the fluids flowing again, so that the tumours cannot start. And I can cure all breast cancers.'

Mention of breast cancer led him to talk of medical problems particular to women. 'There are some who cannot conceive, and others who cannot carry a baby full term. They miscarry at four or five months.'

He offers an explanation.

'With some women the ovaries get blocked. Well, they can be released. In most cases women miscarry because of a blockage of both fluids and blood to the womb. It takes two sessions to correct that. A lot of pregnant women come to me after the first six weeks. I keep the circulation going right.'

Almost as an afterthought he added, 'It takes only two sessions to cure morning sickness.'

I felt a sense, not of incredulity, but of unreality. Here is a quiet man in a quiet house on a quiet hillside, sitting in a room with three chairs, a washhand basin, a bottle of oil and some cotton wool. He is telling me that in his ordinary working day he does things researchers all over the world are investigating – with very mixed success.

There was little time to wonder, none to exclaim, because my host got back to the killer diseases again. This time strokes, with their consequent loss of speech and movement. He is successful too in bringing relief to stroke victims, if not entirely curing them.

'It depends on which part of the nervous system is blocked. The nervous system can easily be cured, providing the brain cells are not dead. Take a person that is paralysed from a stroke or a seizure. At the moment I can cure about forty-five or fifty per cent of the people who come to me. I get people walking who had been paralysed on one side, but it is a slow process, and takes from six to eight months before they get full feeling back.'

His success so far might be the foundation for his sturdy confidence in his diagnosis.

'I have often proved X-rays wrong, even with head tumours. These can be missed by X-rays, especially if they're small. The tumour can be large today, and, because the fluid can go out tonight, you can have a brain-scan the following day and it won't show up. The next day it is back again. The only thing I can do is drain it. I cannot work from the inside. Sometimes the tumours do not fill again, but you cannot guarantee a full cure with most people. If anyone tells you they can, it is ridiculous.'

As might be expected, he receives no medical report with many patients. 'It's very few people I get a medical report about. I have to work it out for myself.'

He explained how he goes about his diagnosis:

'If I am examining a patient for the nervous system it is always the centre finger I use because it is the only finger I can find the nerves in the body with. If I examine the brain, the head, it is the centre finger that I use for that, too, and I can tell whether there are cells dead, blocked, or whatever is wrong with the brain.

'It is the same if a person comes to me that is losing his or her sight or has hearing problems. Again it is just that the muscles close in on the optic nerve. I release the nerve and the sight comes back. But I do all manipulation with my thumb. It is the natural thing for me.'

Have you ever actually restored sight? I asked.

'Yes, I have. One man that was blind for seven years came to me and he can see now. Because all he had was tissue damage around the nerve. An operation wouldn't have solved it.

'I'm treating children for eye and ear trouble and they have improved forty or fifty per cent. I don't know if they will be fully cured because I can never give a guarantee. I just cannot. The only things I guarantee are sinus, migraine and stomach ulcers.'

Nor will Jimmy Conroy guarantee a cure for arthritis. He can do little except relieve the pain.

'With all arthritis I can relieve pain. I can release the whole nervous system so that the patient has not the pain, but will still have stiffness and immobility of the body. I can help osteo-arthritis sufferers, maybe eighty or ninety per cent, but never a full cure. Unless, that is, with children under sixteen or seventeen who are still growing, not mature. Then you can bring back the bone structure.'

He told me a half-sad, half-glad tale.

'I remember one little girl that came here and she was very bad. Her brother was after dying in the hospital, where he went for arthritis. He was allergic to the drug they gave him and he died of a heart attack. The family were very upset, because it was only six months until the little girl was in the same way.

'That little girl is one hundred per cent today. It is great to see somebody, who has no hope, get well. And when people come back and they can walk and their pains are gone, you have achieved something. That really keeps you going. The most important thing is to be able to use the gift to help people.'

When Jimmy Conroy was growing up it was never considered or suggested that he might have a healing gift. Indeed his brothers and sisters have no interest in healing. He has hopes, however, that at least one of his children will have the gift.

It is hardly surprising that his views on bonesetting are different from the usual ones of doctors and hospitals.

'I'm not knocking the medical people, but if you go to a hospital and the bone is set, it is put into plaster and it takes six to eight weeks to set. If a patient comes to me with a broken bone, I manipulate it and release the fluid around it, and the bone will knit in three days. The patient can work with it after seven days, and it only needs a tight bandage to hold it in place.'

I had driven over a hundred miles to meet Jimmy Conroy, and I was very tired by now. It was my own exhaustion that made me feel for the man opposite me, to ask him how he felt at the end of a long day with the pressure of so many people, all in trouble, all needing help, all drawing off his strength.

The answer echoed that of many of the other healers I spoke to. Like them, he too feels energy being drawn from him as he heals.

However, now, it seems he can tell his patients' energy levels by looking at them. 'When I first started treating people, they would go home full of energy, but I would be feeling tired. I was giving them all my energy. I said I'd have to correct that. I couldn't use up all my energy and have enough to keep me going for ten to twelve hours a day.

'Nowadays when I examine a patient I know if all their energy centres are closed so they cannot draw from them. We all have energy centres in our bodies: we have so much electricity in our bodies and this is stored in our energy centres.

'If a person comes to me who has very poor energy, is very weak, I always cross my hands when I'm starting' – he crossed his hands at the wrists, to demonstrate. 'That means you won't give energy to, or take energy from, a patient.

'At the end of the day, if the other patients were not going to take long, I could afford to give energy to a patient. I can do this from my own energy centres. I can give energy to people that are always tired, always fatigued. This is the great thing that I find with my healing – giving this energy, this new lease of life. It only takes one session and it is done through the circulation system.'

He went on to talk about diabetes. 'It is something I have not done an awful lot of. All I can do for diabetics is to work on their circulation so they can live a normal life and have enough energy to keep them going. At least they will never go into a coma.'

When Jimmy Conroy talks of energy centres or the circulatory system, he seems to draw on some instinctive understanding, but he has also put in prodigious amounts of formal study from ordinary medical manuals. However, his theories about energy centres or their implementation find little response from orthodox medical practitioners. 'This is one area that the medical people have lost out on,' he says. 'It is something they find very hard to accept.' Doctors do not, however, allow their unwillingness to accept energy centres to interfere with practical appreciation of the results obtained by Jimmy Conroy: some doctors are in fact patients.

'They bring their families also, because they know this treatment is quite safe. I'm not using drugs and there are no side effects. I cannot, and do not, take any chances with the body.'

And those doctors send their own patients to him.

Jimmy Conroy is willing to co-operate with scientific investigation into what he does. Yet doctors tell him that this will take a long time.

Jimmy Conroy is not registered as a medical practitioner. He could register as a masseur and possibly be paid through the health boards or private health insurance. If poorer people with medical cards come to him, and they do, he takes maybe £1, or nothing at all. From others he may take £5.

And this man could be millionaire if he chose.

As I drove home, the lines of an old jingle kept running through my head. 'If you haven't got a penny, a ha'penny will do, and if you haven't got a ha'penny, God bless you.'

❧ *Putting Bones in Their Place*

DAN O'NEILL is to people with bones out of joint what the AA is to the weary traveller whose car has broken down by the roadside, and who has to limp along for miles on sore feet to get to a telephone.

Myshall, where Dan O'Neill lives, is about five miles outside Carlow town. The directions I was given were complicated, and I got lost several times. Finally, however, I found a couple of signs that led me to a boreen and into the backyard of the man I had come to see.

The place has an air of prosperity: there are solid and cared-for stables and outhouses, probably generations old, and well-tended bright green fields, all clearly cherished and valued.

The O'Neills have been setting injured limbs and bones since the first Elisabeth was on the throne of England. They were at it two hundred years before the French Revolution and the American Declaration of Independence, and two hundred and fifty years before the Great Famine in Ireland. Dan's grandfather set bones; so did his great-grandfather; and that's the way it was for at least four hundred years.

Dan O'Neill never saw a bone set until he began to do it himself. 'My father could not do it. My uncle did it, but he did not live here. I hadn't a clue, starting. I didn't want to start, as a matter of fact.'

Possibly because of his unwillingness and hesitation, the story of how he began is vivid in Dan's memory.

'It was an auctioneer in Tullow that rang up and said his young one had had a fall, and there was something wrong with her arm. My uncle was about three days dead at the time, and so I told him about another uncle of mine. He said, "I don't know these people. I know you, so you'll look at it for me anyhow." I said, "I'll do that all right, but you are wasting your time coming here."

'He brought the child that night, and I looked at her and said, "I think the wrist is out." He said, "Put it back." I said, "I won't. Since you're here now, I'll bring you down to my Uncle Pat."

'"It's in you," the auctioneer said. "Go on and do it." I said, "No." "Don't let the name down," he says to me. "You are the only one left, and I won't leave here till you try it."

'I said, "Fair enough, if you're willing to take the chance, I'll chance it, but don't blame me if it goes wrong." "Oh," he says, "it won't go wrong."

'So I caught the hand and gave it a twist, and it clicked back. "Now," he says, "now, can't you do it? Stay at it now."

'And that was the start of it.'

<hr />

Was Dan O'Neill able to practice all the skills of bone-setting right from that moment – discs, joints, and so on? Did it all come together straight away?

'No. The strange thing is, I'm the first member of my family to do the discs. I was seven or eight years doing the joints, and I wasn't looking at the discs. I wouldn't look at anything like that. One day I happened to go up the road, and this fellow stopped me and told me about a neighbour of his who was in bed with a pain in his back.

'He asked me would I look at it and I said I wouldn't, that I didn't know anything about backs. "Can't he go to a doctor?" I asked. He had already been to one, and he's no better, maybe worse, the man told me. "Well," said I, "the best thing he can do is go to Heffernan in Tipperary. I know nothing about backs."

'"Goddammit," the man said, "amn't I telling you he can't get out of bed! Maybe if you come in you might be able to do something for him, so we could get him to Tipperary." So I went in – it's only a bit up the road. The neighbour was so bad he had to be turned in the bed. About halfway up his back, there was – I still can't explain what it was I saw, but I just put my thumb on it. "Oh, there it is," the man said. I lifted up the leg and I could feel the disc slipping back. He got instant relief. He actually got up and walked around immediately.'

So how did his family acquire the gift all those years ago?

'As far as I'm concerned, it's a gift from God, and I thank God for it every day I get up.'

Dan O'Neill is not the only one to thank God for his gift. In his waiting-room I met some of these thankful people, and some merely hopeful ones. Dan has a farm to run, and sets aside certain hours for patients. There were four people there when I arrived – lots more came later.

One was a dark-skinned dark-eyed woman with masses of black, heavy, wavy hair. She was in great pain. She had taken a toss in a church and had been taken to hospital. 'They done something with my leg in the hospital, but I knew it wasn't right – the pain kept getting worse. So my husband took off the plaster and, look, isn't that a bone sticking out?' We looked, and we felt gently, and sure enough there was something sharp pressing through her very swollen ankle.

A thin-faced, horsey-looking man, with two bright, inquisitive, eyes, leaned over to have a look. He clucked sympathetically.

'Does he take long?' the woman asked. 'He seems to be taking ages with the last one.'

'Don't worry, Missus,' he answered. 'Sure why would he be long? Sure there wasn't that much wrong with the oul' mare to start with. Dan'll be finished with her in a shake.'

The oul' *what*? Is this a joke? I asked myself. A mare? The people in the room seemed to be taking it in their stride. The woman with the ankle wouldn't have cared if Dan O'Neill were fixing giraffes.

I had to ask: Does he treat animals too?

Before anyone could answer, a woman came in and joined us, carrying a small terrier. A dislocated hip, she told us he had. The little dog, cradled in her arms, gave her the odd lick and awaited his turn.

Then I understood. A gift from God, Dan O'Neill had called it, and he evidently makes no distinctions between God's creatures when they come to him for help. It was a satisfying moment, giving me a sense of being at home in the world.

❧

In Ireland there are no registration authorities nor recognised qualifications for chiropractors, spinologists, herbalists or bonesetters. While there is no legal prohibition on persons practising them, these professions are not recognised formally.

But there is an interesting side to this: 'I can give certificates for Social Welfare and for insurance,' Dan says, 'and I have been accepted in court as an expert witness.'

It seems that Dan O'Neill's reputation and proven skill with all kinds of bone problems, and the fact that many sufferers will go to him rather than to a doctor, have resulted in this *de facto* recognition.

'The certificates? Well I just write them and they are accepted. It was questioned. Of course it was questioned. But they are accepted by the Department of Social Welfare. And the insurance companies accept my certs too. I don't know if they accept them from anybody else.'

There is also of course the matter of how the medical profession reacts. 'It's mixed,' Dan says. 'Plenty of doctors send people to me, and some come themselves. More doctors would cut my throat.'

Dan O'Neill was actually putting slipped discs back in place during the time when doctors were still saying discs could not come out. 'That was because they didn't show up on the X-rays,' Dan explains. 'But now, with new developments, they can probably see them.'

There is a price to be paid for all Dan does. His family does not see enough of him, especially when he is busy with bonesetting. While they do not resent this side of his life, they miss a certain amount of his company. And he misses their company too.

Emotionally he can handle it fine, but the physical cost is a different story. The work can be very tiring, Dan says, far more than a comparable job like physiotherapy: 'It takes an awful lot out of you,' he says.

And for this, Dan takes as reward whatever people choose to give him: 'When I was starting, the local curate – we were very friendly – said, "Carry on the same as it has always been. The people of the parish, take nothing off them. And what the rest of them want to give you, do with that."'

As I was leaving the surgery, a very large woman was just arriving. She was uttering a frustrated stream of self-directed recriminations and gasps of pain, and bending over.

She was, she said, a mess: 'You wouldn't believe what an eejit I was. Six discs he put back for me, just a week ago, and, oh Jesus, you'll never believe it, but wasn't I just home and ready to eat a bit when the bloody cat jumped on the table. Well, didn't I make a dive at him, and fell over the so-and-so dog and put the whole lot of them [the discs] out again. I swear to God that if Dan can get them back again I'll get measured for a timber corset and wear it day and night till they set like concrete. I swear.'

With infinite care she lowered herself into a chair.

Afterwards I waited outside in the car, curious to see what this lady would be like when she emerged from Dan O'Neill. She emerged walking for all the world like a soldier marching into a gale-force wind. I thought she might keel over backwards. The discs were back where they belonged, she said, and she had been told not to bend, hence her extraordinary martial gait.

Then came the problem of getting her into the car without bending. Between myself and her brother, who had driven her, one on either side, we slowly folded her into a sitting position and inserted her gingerly into the front seat.

* * *

In Kilbannon, County Galway, the ruins of an ancient round tower watch over the crosses and headstones in the church-yard and cemetery. Most of the graves are of the traditional kind, giving name, date of birth and date of death. Some carry carvings of a hand holding a human bone, the emblem of the bonesetter. These graves belong to the Acton family, a famous family of bonesetters who have lived in this area for at least two hundred years: the present practitioner, P.J. Acton, who runs a shop in nearby Tuam, would not care to go further back than about 1750.

P.J. did not like bonesetting either as a child or as a young man.

'Radio it was that time, there was no television. When my father was working in the room he used, I used to turn up the volume as far as it would go so as not to have to listen to the roaring of some people. I didn't care what the radio programme was as long as I couldn't hear. And no fear I have ever looked at what was going on in the room, never.'

It is strange that having lived with bonesetting and disliking it so much that he is the one member of the family to continue the tradition. Dan O'Neill of Myshall did not want to be a bonesetter either, but he had not lived with it as a boy; his uncles who lived some distance away had been the practitioners, not his father. Like Dan, P.J. Acton's introduction to the craft of bonesetting came about rather suddenly.

When P.J. was a very young man a neighbour who had injured his ankle called to the house seeking Tom Acton's help. Mrs Acton explained that her husband was ill in bed and could not help him. The neighbour persisted: he wanted to see Tom; his advice alone would help. Mrs Acton agreed.

Shortly after the neighbour went upstairs to the bedroom, P.J.'s father called to him. When P.J. entered the room, his father pointed to the neighbour. 'P.J.,' his father said, 'fix that man's ankle.'

It was, P.J. told me, the most extraordinary experience of his life. As if in a dream, he felt he was watching someone else go to the neighbour, take hold of his ankle and go through some motions. It did not seem to have anything to do with him. Yet from that day on he knew what to do to mend sprains and breaks and bones in general, and he simply continued to practice from then on.

The bonesetters art is the most familiar and the most easily understood of the healing gifts, so it was with some surprise that I heard exotic sounding words like 'dragon's blood' and 'Burgundy pitch' fall from P.J.'s lips as he spoke about his craft. They are not ingredients for a wizard's spell; they are, rather, ingredients for plasters that help to cure the bones of the ribs.

'When the ribs are cracked or when they go in – and if they are cracked they must have gone in, so its much the same thing – dragon's blood and Burgundy pitch were always the best cure for that. You cannot get your fingers inside the ribs so you cannot pull them out, but a plaster of these two will do the job.'

Dr Patrick Logan, author of *Irish Country Cures*, says, 'Fractures among the common people were probably treated by the bone setter. In this, the advantage was probably with the common people.'

P.J. tells a humorous but true story concerning his father which may bear this point out.

'My father was in the Regional Hospital in Galway with stomach trouble. The man in the bed next to him had a broken leg and was in a bad state, and the doctors couldn't seem to do much for him. One night my father could not stand the man's moaning and groaning anymore – this was a long time ago and they hadn't the way of controlling pain as they have today. This was back in the forties. Anyway, didn't my father get out of bed one night – the nurses were at supper, I suppose – and he set the poor man's leg properly. In the morning, when the doctors were doing their rounds, they came to the man, who for the first time had had a good night's sleep. Nobody said anything – not the man, nor my father, and the doctors were smart enough to say nothing too. I suppose they knew well enough what my father could do, though they would not let on they did.'

Y OUR DOCTOR SAYS it's not a bug and it's not a virus, so what ails you? Probably an allergy, the doc says. Good. So you're allergic to what?

Ah, but that's the problem. Who knows? Who can tell what you're allergic to?

Allergies can be a very serious matter, which for some people can make life a living hell, sometimes even putting people into mental hospitals. There could be, however, no easier or more enjoyable way of identifying an allergy than by going to Hazel Springs outside Tullow, County Carlow. You seek out a long, elegant bungalow with a swallow's nest tucked into the eaves – said to be the sign of a peaceful and happy home. You will be met by two dogs, one like a man-eating lion, mane and all, but gentle, or so they tell me. The other one is a terrier, noisy and nosy, the kind you very likely have at home. Once there, you ask for Wilfrid Thackaberry, and get him to hold your hand.

Wilfrid Thackaberry is a water diviner whose divining powers extend to allergies. He takes your hand in his, and uses a diviner's pendulum to tell you what you should not eat, or wear, or wash your clothes in, or keep any sort of company with if you want to avoid those rashes, headaches, or whatever it is that afflicts you.

Wilfrid and I are sitting at a large mahogany table that holds a large leather-bound book like a ledger, similar to an *Encyclopedia Britannica* volume, except that it's handwritten. The book contains lists of practically every item of food, drink, clothing, washing-up liquid, shampoos, sprays, polishes, trees, shrubs, flowers, weed killers, fertilisers, dogs, cats, birds, well water, mains water, perfume – in fact, anything you might ever encounter in your everyday life.

My right hand is in Wilfrid Thackaberry's left. His right hand holds the pendulum, poised on its chain above the ledger. The pendulum moves slowly and methodically across and down each page.

So intense is Wilfrid's concentration that I don't dare to interrupt even when the pendulum starts to swing in a circle at the word *chocolate*. A few minutes later it does the same over *brushed nylon*, and then over *oranges*.

The verdict is in and it is right on: brushed nylon bites me and I've known for years about the chocolate. Though I love the stuff, eating it usually brings on a headache or stomach ache.

Now I am free to ask questions. Does he know how the pendulum works? Can he understand it?

'It's the divining.'

You divine allergies from the written word, holding a person's hand. But do you know how it happens? Or why?

'It just happens. I don't know how or why. I just accept it.'

Can you remember, I ask, what started you divining allergies? How did you ever come to think of it, to try it out?

'Well, I was always a water diviner. I suppose the start of doing the allergies was when our daughter had babies that were getting sick. The Missus started writing down what the baby would be using, and I'd go over it with the pendulum.'

I turn to 'the Missus' – Florrie Thackaberry. A warm, gentle lady with a welcoming manner, she has a significant role in all this divining. 'There was a Mr Wilson in Tullow – he's dead now – and he could divine the body,' she tells me. 'So our daughter said, "Daddy, why not try what Mr Wilson does? Try the pendulum on [the allergy list in] the medical book and see if it will work." Well, it did work.

'Then a friend of our daughter's asked Wilf if he would help her too with some allergy. We wrote down a few things that she would be around every day, and the pendulum swung on geraniums. So the girl decided she would do away with her geraniums, but Wilfrid said, no, just put them outside. She did, and she was perfect after that.'

It all began, then, with a few *ad hoc* lists of things that might cause allergies, scribbled on bits of paper. Eventually, Florrie Thackaberry decided to write them into a book which would act as his great source of reference.

'As the names of things came in, I wrote them into the book, one below the other – the ordinary things people use and work with very day. I'm now into the third book. The books get worn from constant use, so when I get time I will sit down and write them out again, and there will be extra things to put into the new books.'

The work takes a lot out of Thackaberry. 'I'm always tired at the end of a session,' he says. 'I'm fairly flat out if I'm doing a lot, and I flop a bit. But I'm very satisfied, very pleased. There's a lot of satisfaction in helping people. The gift would be no good if you didn't help people. But it does affect your life.'

Indeed the divining affects all their lives. Because of the pressure, Wilfrid has had to partly retire from farming.

Florrie: 'It would take over your life if you let it. It changes it. You have to work your life around it. I try to come between Wilf and the work. If I didn't, he wouldn't be able to stick it. You might think it doesn't take anything out of him, but it does. He's tired all the time.'

It has also touched Florrie's life: 'It has changed me, my attitude and outlook, definitely. You look kinder at people – you get more tolerant.'

Both Thackaberrys take an especial joy in easing the pain of infants, who cannot speak for themselves and explain their symptoms. Florrie told of a woman from Wicklow who brought her baby to them: 'She was nearly demented. The baby was crying night and day. Well, the pendulum told us it was the washing-up liquid she was using to wash the baby's bottle. She threw it out and tried another brand: after a week she didn't know herself, the baby was so good.'

Conversation with the Thackaberrys moves easily. One of them can begin a sentence and the other might end it, and you'd hardly notice the changeover, so great is the harmony between them. The atmosphere of peace and friendliness in the Thackaberry home must be a great solace to the people who come for help. It must be especially reassuring for disturbed people – and allergies can leave people very disturbed, even mentally disturbed.

It is hard to accept that an ordinary item of clothing, like a pair of tights, or food, like a simple orange, can make the difference between leading a normal life and one lived in a mental institution, but it can be so.

Wilfrid explains: 'There was a woman who came here to me from the mental home in Cork. She used to be very bad, in and out of the hospital, and her people at home had a bad time from her too. I found that her problem was nylon. She's perfect now: she's been on holiday in the States, and can go anywhere now. And there was a man was equally bad, or mad, and it turned out to be the [medically-prescribed] drugs he was on. He was allergic to them.'

I asked Wilfrid for names of people whose allergies he had divined, so that I could hear their verdicts. Those I talked to would die for him, they feel they owe him so much. For instance Breda Mulcahy, of Avolcore, Midleton, County Cork, was unable to walk, and had been diagnosed as having incurable arthritis. She was only in her early thirties. She wept regularly with the pain. A young man in the neighbourhood brought Breda to see Wilfrid Thackaberry.

'He put me off a lot of things,' she told me when we met. 'I can't eat brown or white baker's bread, only homemade soda bread. No butter — only Flora. No beef. I can have boiled chicken, lean bacon, lean cooked ham, and boiled chops. But no sugar at all, not even sweets unless they are sugar free.

'You would think life would be hard after that, wouldn't you? Well it isn't, because now I can walk, I can run, I can kick a ball and I can dance a lively dance too. Life is just great.'

Wilfrid says that, generally, doctors are well disposed to his methods. 'An odd one doesn't want to hear my name, but only the odd one. Doctors themselves come here for help. One came lately with her own child, who was getting a lot of pain and had been around the specialists and all that, but wasn't improving. I was able to tell her what food to cut out, and she sent back word in a fortnight that the child was fine.'

In fact, one east-coast eye specialist regularly advises his patients to visit Wilfrid Thackaberry when he suspects an allergy affecting the eyes. Does he telephone to say he is sending a patient? I asked.

'No. I actually never met the man. The people tell me when they come, that he sent them. He just tells them straight out – no beating about the bush.'

There is no charge for divining allergies. 'Just a gift from people,' Wilfrid says. 'I don't make a charge: they may give me a present if they want.'

How does this divining of human beings work? Well, how does water divining work? The ability to locate water was as essential to the development of the human race as was the ability to make fire, yet today, though we can walk on the moon, we have no more idea than our remote ancestors did how divining happens. We do not know if the power resides in the diviner or the divined, or in the combination of both. Nobody knows – neither scientist, theologian nor psychologist. The phenomenon is simply observed and accepted, but not understood.

Because Wilfrid held my hand when divining my allergies, I hazarded a guess that my own body was somehow telling me what I should eat or wear – through the diviner and his pendulum. However, as it is in the case of Brian Keelan, the technique works equally well if Wilfrid holds in his hand a photograph of someone. The pendulum responds to photos as it does to the living person. Wilfrid does not understand it any more than I do: 'I'd say it's an energy of some sort. I don't know. Anyway, I'd say it's a natural thing.'

Most of the gift healers I met have been handed down their gift by a family member and they would all like their families to continue the healing tradition. Tradition is literally a *handing down* – from the Latin *tradere*. The Thackaberrys are no exception to this desire, but their gift is. It's exceptional in that it varies its form with the generations. Some generations back, the gift was the stopping of blood. Then it changed to water divining in the next generation, and then the stopping of bleeding returned to the family.

Now it's divining again, but this time of allergies in human beings also, while, almost predictably, young Adrian Thackaberry, Wilfrid's son, is able to stop bleeding.

What is even more curious is that Adrian does not seem to have inherited the gift through his parents or grand-parents. 'That gift,' his mother told me, 'was given to him by a nurse who had been with me when he was born. She became very fond of Adrian, and finally she gave him the gift.'

Adrian remembers one day coming home from school, bleeding badly after a fall. His nurse friend happened to be visiting. 'When she saw me she said, "Why didn't you stop the bleeding? You can stop bleeding in yourself as well as in other people." And she gave me the prayer to say. Since then, I always stop the bleeding with that prayer.'

I wondered on hearing that story whether the nurse had in fact given him the gift, or had she simply discerned that he possessed the gift, and urged him to use it by giving him the prayer.

Can Adrian stop bleeding from a distance? I asked, remembering Brian Keelan's powers.

'Oh, yes,' Florrie answered. 'Very recently there was a German who lives in Fennah, and Adrian saved a very valu-able foal for him. He saved the foal over the telephone, because he couldn't leave the milking to go there. Well the German sent down half a dozen crystal glasses by way of saying thanks. My son really appreciated that, because some people, not too many, do not always say thanks.'

Wilfrid would like his son to try his hand at divining, so that the family could continue helping people with allergies. Adrian says he will do as his father asks, and if he finds he is able to divine, he will welcome his rather special inheritance.

The Man who Cures Cancer

THE FEAR OF getting cancer is higher, apparently, than the actual risk of getting the disease. According to a recent report in the *Cork Examiner*, only one in four hundred people will contact cancer in their lifetime, and many of them survive it. Despite comforting figures, the dread of the disease stalks many people's lives. So, to hear that there is a man who can cure many types of cancers with a plaster, some herbs and an egg seems miraculous indeed. Leslie Deacon is such a man.

Leslie Deacon lives in what must once have been a very imposing house, just outside the village of Bridgetown in County Wexford. He says that he can 'take out the growths of cancer and skin cancer that come on the face and other parts of the body'.

At first, I was a bit put off by the old Georgian house where Leslie lives, not knowing what to expect. A gravel avenue leads to the back of the house, through a swept and tidy yard that has stabling for a good number of horses. There was a deep silence there, and it gave the place a feeling of isolation.

Then, to my delight, two small white-and-tan terriers rushed down the steps, friendliness in every tail wag and frisk and wiggle and lick. My courage was restored and I called out hopefully.

Leslie Deacon was at home. When he came down the wide stone steps from the front door, he didn't look in the least like a character out of *The Irish RM*, which the house had led me to expect. Small and slim, with a pleasant face and a soft manner, he is quiet spoken and very matter of fact.

We went into the house and walked along a passage to the room where he works and keeps the things he uses for the cure. He prefers to talk about the cure, rather than about himself.

It would be hard to imagine a more unlikely setting for the cure of a deadly disease than this old room with its high windows, lofty ceilings and lovely plasterwork. It could have been 1788, not 1988. Even the ingredients on the table – the bottle of herbs, the egg – seemed the same as they would have been two hundred years ago. The sense of time warp was heightened by the absence of machine-made noises. The atmosphere of timelessness was also heightened by the subject I had come to hear about, which, however easily Leslie Deacon copes with it, is grim and heavy and fearful – life and death.

He says that he is detached from the whole thing, that it takes nothing out of him in a personal way. But almost in the same breath he told me that I'd have had some job to talk to him outside of his house. 'Once I leave this table I leave all this after me,' he said. 'In fact I wouldn't talk to you down on the road.'

Since we were not down on the road, however, he did talk to me.

'There was a woman who was within ten weeks of giving birth to her child,' Leslie started. 'The cancer was on the top of her breast, but not very much under the skin. I can take it off if it is this deep.' To demonstrate, he wrapped a paper handkerchief around a pencil, about a quarter of an inch from the top. 'But if it was that deep,' he said, moving the handkerchief down about an inch on the pencil, 'I could do nothing. It would take the whole breast off. Nobody could stand the pain.

'Well, about this woman. After checking with a medical friend, I put the plaster on, and a month later she gave birth to her child and breast-fed it.'

❦

Leslie (he warned me that he does not care to be addressed as Mr Deacon) was reared with his grandmother from the age of two. This lady, for reasons of her own, bought the cure from another woman, also a Deacon. William Rigley, the man who brought the cure into the Deacon family, was possibly the husband or father of the woman who sold it. The Rigley family may have been anxious to get rid of it, as 'William and another man went to Dublin to take a cancer off somebody there,' and, the Deacon tradition goes, 'they got drunk and got killed' in an accident.

Leslie was too young to have been given the gift by his grandmother before she died. So his uncle, Willie, had the gift until his death, a little over three years ago. It has now been about ninety-five years in Leslie's branch of the family.

There is a lot of work in the preparation of the ingredients of the cure. 'Ninety-nine per cent of what I use is herbs. Everything I do is out of the earth, even the egg.' The egg he spoke of is the yoke of an egg in the half-shell which was on the table.

'I have to go out and pick the herbs and dry them in the sun. Then I grind them down and I roll the dried herbs with my hands and then sieve it. Lately I got a blender and that helps. But I have to buy the plasters – that big roll costs about £4.60, and the one beside it is £4, and so on. And then some people come in for cures, maybe they come three or four times, and walk out and give nothing.'

I wondered if there is any formal or traditional passing on of the gift to cure and to diagnose cancer. Had Leslie's uncle perhaps said, 'I'm giving you this gift now,' or anything like that?

'It was just the recipe he gave me. I have the gift myself. I'd say I inherited it. The gift is really to know what you are doing. And to know if it is skin cancer.'

Leslie has no doubts about the accuracy of his diagnosis. He didn't even have doubts with the very first person that came to him after his uncle's death. His only doubts were about his own ability to do the right thing at the right time.

I pressed him: Have you any idea how you know when it is cancer?

'No. I don't. No. I don't know how I know. But if I was at the races and among a thousand people, and somebody there had it, I'd see it: it would be the first thing I'd see. 'Twould be in front of my eyes all the time I'd be there.'

Nevertheless Leslie had been uneasy about that first person. 'This is a bit of a story. When my uncle died he had put a plaster on this girl, on her jaw, and didn't it fall off in three days, and wasn't Willie dead in the three days. The girl was in an awful state, but a friend of hers found out it was me had the cure. So I put a plaster on for her, and I'll never forget that while I'm alive. It wasn't easy for me, till she came the second time. I remember that more than any other person ever I did. She was the grandest girl you ever laid eyes on, and it was a marvellous job.'

I was learning a little. Like, that people had to come back a couple of times. On average, how long does it all take?

'I put on the plaster, and the person takes it off in ten days and poultices it with white bread, and that lump or growth will come out. The length of time varies. It's roughly a fortnight, but it could be three weeks in some places, depending on if it is deep or a long time there.'

Leslie's training to practise the cure took the form of observing his grandmother as a child. "Sure I was reared with my Grannie. I'd seen it done thousands of times."

His uncle's death and his inheritance of the gift transformed Leslie Deacon's life. He describes himself as an ordinary man who happens to cure skin cancer, helping people as best he can. Few would agree with his estimate of himself. It is not ordinary to stay at home every evening from 6 to 8 o'clock, and from 11 o'clock in the morning on Sundays until 5 in the afternoon. These hours are elastic, and the weekday 8 o'clock can stretch to 9 or 10. And Sunday may become Monday when there is a crowd.

'It has taken over my life,' Leslie says, 'because you must be home. If I was at your house and there was music – and I love music – I still couldn't stay. I'd have to come back here. You can't leave people waiting. I wouldn't have taken on the cure if I was going to do that.'

Nor is it just a matter of mixing the herbs and the egg, attaching the mixture to the plaster, putting it on the patient, and saying 'next please'.

'You have to take your time at my job. It's not my idea to get them in and out. I sit down and talk to them, especially if they're nervous.

'I remember a chap who had a growth up in his nose. At first I thought it wasn't worth my while putting a plaster on him. But his father and uncle came in here with him, and talked about it, the same as any father would. He was just twenty years old. He came back that day three weeks, and the growth was gone. The plaster comes away with the thing attached to it.'

The cure is for external use only, Leslie says. I questioned if it might not be possible to use his method on internal growths, with the aid of modern technology. 'No. It cannot be used inside. The plaster wouldn't stick, because of the moisture.'

There could be ways of overcoming that, I ventured.

'No. I've had people with it on their tongues, and they had to keep their tongues out all day, or as long as they could, and at least for three hours.

'Look.' And he held in his hand two small greyish looking things. 'This came out of a woman's back.' I was trying not to see. 'And this came out of a woman's jaw.' Reflectively he added, 'I've often seen them bigger than this.'

The recipe for the cure is a secret, and will remain one. 'I want it to remain in our family. I have nieces and nephews, though they might not want to be tied down with it. The chances are that when I hand on the recipe I will hand on the gift of diagnosis with it.'

Leslie has never been approached by doctors about the cure. 'But even if they did approach me, it wouldn't be any good for them, because I wouldn't tell them.'

Why not? I asked.

'I wouldn't tell them, and I wouldn't talk to them either. They would want to know what was in that,' he pointed to the small bottle of greyish powder on the table, 'and that's what they'll never know.'

You wouldn't want to see more people cured with your cure? I asked.

'I would, but not by doctors.'

If the government thought it worthwhile investigating your cure, and were to ask you to co-operate in the search, and of course pay you, what would you say?

'No. I'd say No. I wouldn't give it for the whole of County Wexford.'

Why are you not willing to share your cure?

'I don't know why I hold back, but the hold-back is there.'

You think no money would induce you to tell?

'I don't have to think. I said I would not give it for the whole of County Wexford, and I mean that. My uncle and my grandmother felt the same way.'

It seems to be a very precious inheritance, I said. Is it?

'Yes. It is. I want it in my family.'

Would you not share it to heal people?

'NO.' It was the biggest NO you could get.

I persisted: You cannot be sure that it would work for other people, as you have never told it, never revealed it. Anyway they could not diagnose, could they?

He made a slight concession. 'No. They could not diagnose. That is personal to me.'

A doctor or a chemist could have got one of your plasters, could have got them many times over the years. With modern methods the contents could be broken down in a few minutes. Yet the chances are that it wouldn't work for them. Do you agree?

'I don't know that. It worked for my uncle and Grannie.'

Normally doctors do not diagnose cancer without a sample, while Leslie diagnoses without any technical aids.

'I cannot understand why a doctor cannot diagnose something without taking a piece of it,' he says. 'Doctors have said to people, talking about me: "Deacon cannot know, when he cannot diagnose it." One doctor said to this fellow, "Do you think it was cancer at all? Sure how could he know when he had no way of testing it?"

'Well, I would know. I'd know by it. And I'd know by the feel of my hands as well. If it was on the nose, inside, and I couldn't see very well, I'd know by the feel of my hands.'

Though reared by his grandmother, Leslie had never touched anybody by way of diagnosis until his uncle died. The first person he diagnosed was the girl he told me about earlier, and he was as confident in his diagnosis then as he is now.

I think there is much more to your gift than appears at first hearing, I remarked to Leslie. It is not as simple as it looks, I suggested. It may be simple for you to do, but there is something deeper there.

'I never thought of it that way. I just do it.'

Leslie will not touch anything that doctors have already scraped, or that they have cut. Nor will he deal with people who have had radium treatment.

'Anyone that comes here and who has had it cut, I wouldn't do anything for them, though it was not a success in my opinion. When the doctors cut it, it spreads all around, goes off everywhere.

'There are two people coming to me now, and they have it on their fingers. They came to me about a month or six weeks after the doctors were at them. I told them I would not guarantee it. I'd rather miss them, but their wives persuaded me to put the plasters on.'

But you said you would not touch anything the doctors had touched, I reminded him.

'Yes, but the doctors had not cut them. They wanted one man to go into hospital to get it scraped, but he wouldn't.'

How can you be sure that you would not be successful even after tissue had been removed for analysis?

'Ah. It was tried long before I got the cure.'

Are you one hundred per cent successful?

'Yes. I think so. That's the truth.'

One common trait among the gift healers is the joy they derive from helping people.

'Oh, I did welcome the gift. I've no regrets about getting it, not one in the world, even though it has affected my life. I'm dedicated to it. There is a great delight in helping people. It's a great joy when people go out cured. It makes me very, very happy – happy because they are happy.'

As far as Leslie knows, nobody else in the country can cure skin cancer. 'I have people from England, Wales and Belfast, and from seven or eight counties around. If there was anybody else curing in Dublin or London, they wouldn't be coming here.'

The gift, Leslie supposes, must come from God. 'After all, you couldn't work very well without Him.' But he has no particular religious sense about the whole thing. 'No religion, no prayer, no politics, no nothing!'

There is no charge for the cure. Leslie takes whatever people give him. Sometimes that is nothing.

'I had a girl here – she had it on the arm, a good lump as big as a green pea. Because it was in an awkward place, the plaster didn't stick, and I had to put it on four times before it stuck. She knew my hours well, and still she came here at nearly 11 o'clock at night.

'I remember well the night she left here cured. It was in the month of June, and she didn't even say thanks, not to mention money. She didn't even send me a Christmas card, and, to make it worse, she isn't young.

'I was going to write to her, and tell her what I thought of her, but what was the use in spending another twenty-eight pence!'

When I walked in on Leslie Deacon, everything was ready. It would be natural to assume that he had his impedimenta prepared and ready for me to see. However, the fact is that I was not expected. I had been unable to contact him by telephone and I was unwilling to write and take the chance of being refused an interview, or of not being answered at all, so I went without any arrangements whatsoever. The preparations were for the people who would be coming. And they do come, lots of them.

The people who come to Leslie Deacon have one thing in common: fear. It takes unusual courage to meet that fear maybe seven days a week, year in, year out, to confront it and disarm it. Leslie Deacon has that courage.

TO MANY OF us, an herb is something you throw into the pot to bring out the flavour in your dinner. However, for centuries herbs were mainly used to heal illnesses, and they still form the base of many of the prescribed drugs we may take. It is unlikely these days that we would be told by our doctors to go home and infuse some rosemary for our blocked sinuses, or drink some chamomile for that tummy bug, yet there are people who use herbs in this way, and Sean Boylan is one of them. He also has the gift of diagnosis and the gift of manipulating joints and bones. In his spare time he trains the all-Ireland-winning Meath Gaelic football team.

It is a long story, at least two hundred years long. Four of Sean Boylan's herbal remedies go back to a little cottage in Tara, County Meath, where his great, great-grandfather lived and worked and had his herb garden. That ancestor might be amazed if he could see his great, great-grandson's home, with its walled garden, well-kept drive and rich fields, or witness the air of security and privilege that is one's first impression of the Boylan home in Dunboyne, County Meath.

There is more to it than that. There are the cars parked outside, where people often sit all night, waiting to be early into Sean Boylan's waiting-room in the morning. There are the diagnostic and healing gifts that Sean Boylan puts freely at the service of all who come; there is the total commitment he gives to his patients; there is the extraordinary pace at which he works. At the back of the Boylan house there are ten acres given over to the herbs that Sean uses, as well as four huge polythene tents where the more delicate herbs are grown. It is a large undertaking, with workers employed to tend the herbs.

But the waiting-room is where you learn about Sean Boylan. I sat there, pondering the few things I knew about herbal remedies, like using dock leaves to cure nettle stings. As in all the waiting-rooms of these gift healers, the atmosphere is easy, chatty, cheerful. People exchange tales of illness, doctors, hospitals, triumphs and failures of curing, and the cures of the healer they have come to see.

There are the old hands who regale the first-timers with tales of hours of waiting. If Sean Boylan needs to spend a long time with someone, he does just that. So people are resigned to waiting, because they know that when their turn comes they will get all the time they need with Sean. I was there to listen and observe, and I was to wait until the last patient had gone before meeting with Sean, so I saw and heard plenty.

There was John, a youngish man with a round face, balding head and a neat beard. He seemed cheerful, in spite of the interminable wait. 'You can't have far to travel,' someone said to him, 'or you wouldn't be so cheerful about the delay.'

'I don't care if I have to wait till morning,' John said, 'and neither would you, if you had my story to tell.'

His story was this. He was a jeweller by trade; he designed his own jewellery and made his own moulds, selling to the trade. He had been a happy and successful man, with a thriving business, a comfortable home, a wife and three children, when he had become ill with a rare glandular disease for which there is no known cure. Five years was all the doctors gave him: 'Five years to live – maybe they should have said five years to die.'

He became bedridden, able only to sit propped up with pillows for a few hours each day. Then he couldn't do even that. Everything went – business, home, the lot. All that remained to him was the certainty that he was dying. Then one day a friend decided to take him to see Sean Boylan. 'I hadn't the strength to argue with him,' John remembers. 'Himself and a few more lads lifted me into the back of a station wagon, and put me lying on a mattress, and took me here.

'Sean Boylan examined me, and I'll never forget what he said. He said he couldn't cure me, but he'd make my life tolerable. And he did – by God he did. That was five years ago – I've been taking his herbs since then, and if I stopped I'd go back to the way I was. And, by the way, I'm back in business again.'

Two nuns sat quietly at the far side of the room, slightly apart from the rest of us. Their calm, neutral faces seemed pleasantly interested in everyone, but revealed nothing about themselves. They did not seem to mind the delay.

I went to the ladies' room, and as I was washing my hands, one of the nuns came in. We chatted about the weather, and she asked if this was my first visit to Sean Boylan. She told me it was her third, and that she was a sister from the Bon Secours Hospital in Glasnevin, Dublin.

But, I said, you have the choice of specialists of all kinds in your hospital. Why come here?

'It's something I picked up in India,' she said, 'and it has responded to none of the treatments from any of the doctors. I don't know if Sean can cure me completely either, but already the pain has eased, and I have much more energy.'

Finally came my turn to meet Sean Boylan. As manager-trainer of the twice all-Ireland-winning Meath team, and as a famous healer, I was expecting someone with a deservedly high opinion of himself. I had decided to tread gently, but there was no need for such caution; Sean's quiet and gentle manner put me at ease immediately. He seemed too busy to have opinions about himself. In fact he needed prompting and pushing from me, to get him to talk about himself at all.

'I don't think too much of myself. Maybe I'm someone who has a certain talent, but I wouldn't think I know it all. I wouldn't be afraid to look further for advice or assistance from other people. I've done that many times.

'I remember once talking to a chap I met at an international meeting. He could recognise over 1,400 plants. We were talking over a cup of tea during a break. He was saying, "You're the Irish boy – I've heard of you," and so on. We talked about his knowledge of plants: he knew so much about them, but had no chance to practise healing. I only knew a limited number of plants, but I knew them very well. So each one to his own.'

When talking to Sean Boylan, what comes across is his sense of commitment, his concern for the people who come to him and his conviction of the validity and integrity of herbalism itself. And especially his awareness of his other gift – that of diagnosis.

Sean remembers clearly when he first realised he could diagnose illness. 'I was very young at the time. It was a man who had been told by two doctors he should have a kidney removed. I disagreed. The man left the kidney be, and eventually his TB cleared up."

I pressed him about his diagnostic gift, and he began reflecting on it. 'Obviously it was something that was there in me, and came out with practice. You'd say to the person, this is what's wrong, and they'd say, yes, yes, that's it. To me it has a lot to do with touch. It is a knowledge that has been refined over the years, with all the people coming to me.'

Sean did not initially welcome his gift of diagnosis and healing. 'I did not look on it as a gift for a long time. It can cause problems, and you say to yourself, why me? You'd wish it was a hundred miles away, because you'd have no privacy. You couldn't go here or there without people asking you questions. At the same time, you couldn't walk away from it.

'There were times, when I was a young man – not so much now – and I wanted to do so many things with my life, but the demand was always there. People kept coming and coming, and you'd say to yourself, how can I go on doing this? But you couldn't turn them away.

'But it has also brought me a lot of happiness. Pain, yes, but a lot of happiness. It is a part of yourself, part of your being. You give so much of yourself. But that's where the happiness lies.'

Even the herbal aspect of Sean Boylan's work was taken on reluctantly. Although it was part of the family tradition, and his father practised as an herbalist, Sean had not planned to follow in his footsteps. General farming was more to his liking.

'I was away in agricultural college and one day I rang home and my father answered. I had never thought of my father as getting on in years, but the voice on the phone was the voice of an old man. It shocked me. I rang home again and said I was coming home. That was in 1961. I came home to give him a hand, and I'm still here.'

Unlike some of the other healers I encountered, Sean seems to have a harmonious relationship with the medical profession: 'A lot of them send patients to me, but some are sceptical because they are not aware of what particular plants can do. Naturally such would feel they have to protect patients that go to them, but in many cases a great rapport has grown up between certain medical people and myself, and this has led to a sharing of knowledge. This is healthy, it's a balance, the way nature should be. Nobody has all the answers.'

I asked him what he could do that conventional medicine could not.

'Our ultimate aim is the same – to get somebody right. Say somebody has a gallstone condition that can't be operated because of a heart condition. If I can give herbal medicine that will dissolve the stones, I can give comfort and a lease of life they wouldn't otherwise have. And there are certain chest and stomach conditions that can't be cured, but I can give them relief, and keep the person going on a fairly decent level of health.'

There is, as yet, no school of herbalism in Ireland. Britain has two. One, in Tunbridge Wells, offers a four-year diploma course that is state registered and recognised by the medical profession; there is also a correspondence course for non-professionals. Has Sean Boylan ever considered setting up a school of herbalism here? There is little encouragement for him to do so. In Ireland there is not even an herbalist association. Nor does the state show any recognition of herbalists, for instance, through the social welfare or public health system. Those who come to Sean Boylan must pay for themselves. Yet, while Sean has no plans to train herbalists, he believes there would be very few problems with the medical profession if anyone were to do so. 'The medics might be wary, but that wariness might not be for selfish reasons. They would want to protect people, but once the ultimate aim of herbalism was right – to relieve pain and suffering – there would be no problem.'

Herbal healing is not, he emphasises, an alternative to orthodox medicine. 'There is a place for both, and that is slowly being recognised. Medicine as we know it tends to be a closed shop. We forget that two-thirds of the world doesn't know medicine as we have it, and yet they survive.

'Anyway, even in the mechanical miracle of modern medicine, there should still be a place for the human thing. Sometimes specialisation can be carried too far. So you could have a terrible pain in your hip, and a stomach disorder at the same time. One doctor will look after the hip and another will see to the stomach. But if the stomach has been bad for a long while, maybe you're getting a lot of acid and have an osteo condition. We forget that the body is one unit, from top to toe, and herbalism deals with that one unit.'

Is there ever a danger that herbal remedies can react badly with prescribed drugs a person is already taking? Say someone is taking medical drugs for ulcers, and gets herbal treatment for an allergy?

Sean Boylan: 'You have to be very well aware of manufactured drugs, so that what you give will not clash with them. It is important to realise that what can do good could also do harm. And there are things like belladonna which is marvellous for broken bones and the relief of pain, but I won't use it, because it is basically a deadly poison – the deadly nightshade.'

Sean has one great advantage, in that he grows most of the herbs himself. What he does not grow, he knows where it comes from, and everything is grown in Ireland, bar one plant from the Lebanon. Lack of research makes it difficult to find reliable figures for the numbers of people turning to herbal remedies, but the growing trend for health-food shops and natural remedies indicates an increasing demand for them.

'There is a huge swing back to the natural methods,' Sean says, 'because of the fears about modern drugs. Thousands of people have come here to me. It's not because they like me. There's a free medical service down the road, yet they come here, and pay for what I make up for them. They come because they weren't cured, and they believe I can do it.'

Sean charges no fee for the consultation. 'We only charge what it costs to produce the product,' he says.

What about rights or patents for cures a herbalist might discover? Is there a danger that a lone herbalist might have his discovery taken up by all and sundry?

Sean Boylan says the World Health Organisation became concerned about this some years ago. 'In 1979 they set up a group to study the matter, and they had people brought together from twenty-nine countries. I was one of the two from Ireland. This body met a number of times.'

But Sean thinks it had little effect, and, anyway, the more human, generous, free-and-easy attitude of the herbalists has great advantages. 'I can just write to somebody in Alabama, and he will talk about his ideas and discoveries, and I can share mine. Whereas if a big company were to put a new drug on the market it could cost about £15 million. The discoverer could be dead and buried before it hit the market.'

Sean Boylan sees herbalism as having its roots deep in folk history. 'You were told as a child that this fruit or that berry could be eaten, but you didn't eat that other one. Herbalism is just an extension of that basic folk experience: such a thing is good for this ailment, and that's it.'

Of course it has its limits: 'There are terminal illnesses we cannot cure, but even then we can sometimes help. Some forms of arthritis can be cured, but to say we can cure everything would be awfully strong words. We can't, of course. And also, in many cases too much damage has been done to bones and joints. But it is good to be able to give relief even then.'

And the cosmetic side of herbalism, the potential to produce perfumes, lotions, scents and so on; does this interest him? 'There is a vast market there, which would be financially very rewarding. But I'm not in it, because my heart is somewhere else.'

🔥 Releasing Trapped Nerves

M Y FRIEND MONA, her face an off-grey colour, slowly got into the car. 'That man hasn't human fingers at all,' she said. 'They're made of steel. O God, I wish I was at home!'

Earlier that day she had gone to her doctor with a bad pain in her left arm. He had confessed that he could do nothing for her: 'It's a trapped nerve,' he told her. 'You need manipulation or traction.'

She was beginning to lose the power in her arm, and also down her left side. She was frightened, almost desperate.

Enquiries brought news of one Jimmy Connolly, a healer who frees trapped nerves. He had a room over a pub in Galway city, and attended there from around 3 p.m. every day. A telephone call confirmed he would be there that day, so, worried and apprehensive, but hopeful, we set off.

A thin, fair-haired man in his early sixties, with a friendly, relaxed manner, Jimmy Connolly's matter-of-fact attitude eased Mona's fears. He seemed sure of himself and of what he could do.

Like a neutral observer in a war zone, I sat well away from the action as the treatment began. Mona lay face down on a table, as Jimmy Connolly worked on her. Only the moans and gasps from my friend, and the perspiration and air of concentration on the man's face, indicated that anything more than a routine massage was in progress. I moved closer to get a better look. Jimmy Connolly's fingers flew up and down the woman's back, pausing, stabbing, pressing, and moving away again. The right hand seemed to race the left, as if they were in competition with one another.

Afterwards, as Mona was recovering, Jimmy told me how he had come to recognise and appreciate his gift. His air of competence, of being in control, probably dates from his years as a sergeant in the army, where he was a physical-training instructor. Even his way of speaking has echoes of the parade ground.

'I was a PT fanatic all my life, and began to box when I joined the army. I was sent to the Curragh Army Camp on a PT course, and things I learned there made me interested in the body. So I studied it a bit, never dreaming, though, that I'd go in at the deep end.'

He spoke slowly, remembering. On leaving the army, Jimmy joined the ESB, and was stationed in Loughrea. With his interest in sports it was not long before he became involved with the local hurling team. It was around this time that he began working with injuries: 'I used to do bits and pieces with the team, before the match, and during and after. Putting back fingers and fixing sprains – that sort of thing.'

Strangely enough, Jimmy Connolly's compassion for injured people, which was later to play such a dominant role in his life, was not uppermost in his mind at that time. It was simply a matter of getting players ready to play again. Nor did he feel he had any special gift.

He should have been aware, because, years before, his mother had said to him: 'There's something in your hands, Jimmy, and some day you will find it. Uncle Joe was a bone-setter, and of all the family, you are most like him. The rest are on your father's side, but you are a Coye.' It didn't dawn on Jimmy to question his mother, and he hardly understood what she had been talking about until much later.

But your mother was right, I said.

'She was right. It was in the hands, in the family. It is a passed-on skill, a throwback, but I have no idea how far back it goes. I gradually learned I had the hands for it. The hands *are* it. I have extraordinary strength in my hands, light though I am.'

Mona interrupted. 'Will the pain ever go?' she asked plaintively.

'It will go. By the time you get home it will have started to wear off, but you will need maybe two more treatments. I can only do so much at one time. It would be too severe for you. But you will sleep tonight.'

Mona did sleep that night, and within a fortnight, following two more punishing treatments, became as well as ever.

I asked Jimmy to describe his gradual realisation that he had the gift.

'What happened was this: there was a vacancy in the Corrib Great Southern Hotel for a masseur. They wanted someone to look after the sauna and the visitors — a masseur-cum-physiotherapist. I had left the ESB by then, and I got the position. The hotel allowed non-residents to come for treatment. I had all sorts of people, including film stars like Paul Newman.

'By the time I finished there, I knew I had the gift for healing trapped nerves, as well as for setting bones. Then

Tim Richardson offered me a room over his pub, and here I am. No advertising – I never advertised – just word of mouth.'

Did Jimmy welcome his gift?

'I did, and I still do. It is great to meet people ten or fifteen years after, and they to say to you, Look at me now. The pride I take in that! It is a mighty satisfaction. I went into the discs and backs and so on. It all ties up – the bones and the nerves. The hip and shoulder can be out, and the muscles very much involved there. Everything has to go back where it came from.'

Jimmy explained that people with new injuries can be cured with fewer treatments, sometimes only one. 'But an injury of, say, twelve months or more generally takes about three visits, and also there are exercises to be done before these people are completely all right. But it is lovely to see people coming in on sticks or crutches, and walking out without them.'

Would many of Jimmy Connolly's patients have been to see doctors?

'Oh, God, yes. That's the killer – the tablets and the needles and the doctors keeping them for so long, and knowing they can do nothing for them. That's the killer, they don't be sent to me in time.'

But, I challenged, there are doctors who specialise in bones and backs. Some of them must be good.

Jimmy would have none of it: 'It's not in their hands. They must go to the books all the time. They are book-worms, trained to deal with brain and tummy, and they know of tablets for swollen joints, and so forth. But they haven't the sense of touch.'

But physiotherapists are trained to use their hands, I argued.

'Maybe they are, but they don't seem to manage nerves. You see, all the muscles in your body, in the legs, arms, the whole lot, are intertwined and you can get a nerve trapped in between them. You must move the muscles to release the nerve, and leave them back again into their own positions.

'A muscle can get into a ball and trap a nerve. You have to break up the muscles and smooth it out to release the nerve. And that is hand work, all hand work, and you need the instinct to do it right.'

Jimmy was in full flight, powered by impatience and indignation: 'Doctors do not believe in people like me. If they stopped to think how people got on before they came – the likes of me were here before they were heard of. And there were herbs before your tablets came. Would they ever stop and think of that? No.'

I found it hard to accept that highly trained medical people, with knowledge of every nerve and muscle in the human body, could not do what Jimmy Connolly claimed to do from instinct or inherited gift. I said so.

Jimmy had an answer: 'You might think this is funny, but I actually get a signal. If I go up along the vertebrae, say, between the top of the vertebrae and the coccyx, I get a signal as my fingers move up and down. I can put my finger on it, like a water diviner. I can put my finger on exactly where the trouble is.'

Is that the gift, the bit the doctors lack?

For answer, he told me a story. He was at a social function in Galway one evening, and there was a girl there in a wheelchair, over on a visit from England. 'I don't know what put it into my head, but I walked over to her. "You don't mind if I help you for a few steps?" I asked. "No," she said. So I put the tips of my fingers to hers, just like that' –

Jimmy put his finger tips against mine – 'and I said, "Come with me now, and don't break the signal," I told her.

'She stood up and followed my hands all the way down to the end of the bar, and back again to the wheelchair. Everybody was dumbfounded.'

Was she able to walk on her own after than?

'Unfortunately she was going back to England the next day. So I got her to walk again, and asked somebody to take a photograph and show it to her doctors over there, but I never heard from her again. I'm certain I would have been able to do something for her.'

That was one of the sad moments, and Jimmy Connolly has had his share of those. 'Those you fail with. People come in without confidence, and then will not do what I tell them, or do the exercises I give them. I say, don't bother coming back – we're not together on this.

'Age will beat you as well. You have to watch the heart, and the blood clots, so many things to watch.

'And you worry, oh, you do. Did I do the right thing, or did I give the right exercises, or will they be too strenuous? You find something to worry about, until you see that patient again.

'You need a grey head before you are fully confident of what you are doing. And you need to be very good before you touch someone's back. Put a finger wrong and you can cripple.'

Jimmy has no idea how he understands hearts or clots, any more than how he understands nerves and muscles, but he says that when he is testing the back or shoulder, he 'gets the heartbeat'. Then he knows exactly how much that heart can take, with the same certainty a doctor will have after using a battery of advanced technology.

So is it magical?

'No. It's straight from the mind. But it wears you out. With, say, a back problem, it saps every bit of energy and electricity in my body. The result is that I couldn't just say next please. I have to go down and have a cup of coffee, or whatever, to relax myself and recharge, and maybe have a chat. If someone says they're in a hurry, it won't work. I have to feel able.'

What about the people who are too bad to come to him?

Jimmy Connolly goes to them. 'If it's Castlebar or Timbuctu, I'd go. The one thing I have to do is follow pain. I can never turn my back on it. I'd go any hour of night or morning. I feel compelled.'

This seems to be a characteristic Jimmy Connolly shares with other gift healers – a sense of obligation to use their gift in the service of people.

What about regrets? Has he any about the way he has lived his life?

'If I had the chance I'd do it all again, only in a different way. I should have based myself somewhere really permanent, but I always had itchy feet. I suppose life would have been different without the gift. But then, I'm not married, so I'm not afraid of the bank manager. I'm over sixty now, and what could I look forward to, only healing? And thank God I'm strong enough.

'This is something to come to every day. People also come to my home, and even downstairs in the pub in the evening, while I'm having a pint and a chat.'

So how does Jimmy Connolly see himself – as a healer or a masseur?

'Sometimes I think I'm an eejit. The pains I take in order to help people. But nine-tenths of the time it is great satisfaction. And for the years I have left, I might as well spend them helping people.'

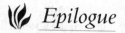 *Epilogue*

THESE ARE THE gift healers as I met them, and as I think of them. In this chapter I will tell what other people think of them and try to offer some theories of my own.

This chapter, too, will ask questions. As for answers, there are only a few, and partial at that, and most of them lead into a maze of bewildering paths where I have not had a glimpse of the exit. Neither, it seems, has anyone else.

Take May Dempsey's cure for brucellosis. It looks so simple that it would be tempting to dismiss it as a fluke, an accident appreciated and seized by a smart man or woman in the long ago and passed on to the family almost as a property would be, in trust for future generations.

A closer look shows that it may be something quite different. Consider this: a weed is rubbed in the hand of a woman, May Dempsey, and then put into ordinary cold water – tap, barrel or well water, it matters not. The mixture will immediately test for the disease and, if the result is positive, will then begin the cure. This must surely be one of the earliest examples of an all-in-one economy pack.

The plant will not tolerate gloves, and will not even remain in the room while the healer is wearing them. The human touch seems to be essential, for whatever reason.

There is an air of briskness and efficiency about this cure that makes it difficult to attribute to blind chance. However, if it was devised and established by intelligence, who or what is this intelligence? Did it go away or is it still around? We do not know.

What about the transmission of these gifts from one generation of a family to another? Long ago, somebody's personality or hair colour or bad temper would often be summed up as being 'in the blood'. This expression has now been replaced by the familiar – if not so well understood – expression 'It's in the genes'.

To learn what science thinks about the role of genes in the transmission of gifts, especially healing gifts, I went to see the distinguished geneticist, Dr Seamus Hanraghan of Tuam, County Galway.

We get from our parents at least 10,000 genes, he explained, but we are not exclusively products of our genes: we are the result of both genes and environment.

'Things like the length of arms or legs result from many genes all operating together,' Dr Hanraghan explained. 'But whether we are fat or thin depends also on the culture in which we have grown up, and on how much we eat and what kinds of food we eat. In short, our environment.' We have an environment even before we are born. He instanced the babies of drug-using mothers who are born with a severe addiction.

To actually determine how important genes are, in terms of inherited traits, would require elaborate and quite impossible experiments. Elaborate, in that they would require controlled breeding arrangements over several generations –

detailed statistical analysis of parents and offspring and then their offspring. Whereas this has been done with white mice and mayflies in laboratory situations, it is impossible that women, men and children can be kept in these conditions. 'We can't do that with humans,' Dr Hanraghan says, 'and perhaps it is just as well.'

The main problem, however, is that we cannot define exactly what healing ability is. 'If you want to investigate something, you have to be able to measure it. I'm not saying these things do not exist. I simply do not know, and there is no way, in terms of conventional rationality, that I can understand how these things happen. So I would not know how to measure them, and neither would anyone else.'

Dr Hanraghan stresses that there are certain areas of existence that his training does not let him perceive. 'My perception of the world's reality is driven by my own training in quantitive science. I have to admit there can be a whole range of other phenomenal realities I cannot see, simply because they do not fit into my mind. There are dimensions we do not perceive because they are not currently amenable to conventional science. My first reaction is, I have to see the evidence. And generally speaking, nobody can produce the evidence. So I do not lose any sleep over it, beyond saying, it is possible.'

The most extraordinary healing power I have come across is the stopping of blood.

Blood is life. Our deepest emotions are often expressed in reference to blood. Love, hate, grief – He shed His blood for us; I'd give my heart's blood to save her; I'll have his blood.

It is not easy to grasp that this amazing power of stopping blood has been directed across oceans, over mountain ranges, valleys and cities, into one room out of all the millions in Dallas, Texas, as it was with Brian Keelan's 'long-distance' patient. Or that it could locate one girl on an operating table and stop, not one, but two haemorrhages.

The surgeon told the patient afterwards that another vein ruptured as he was tying off the first one. He had not expected to save her. He had never before had such and experience, he told her.

The woman has a souvenir – a numb spot on her arm.

For an explanation – if such were possible – I went to see Dr Tom O'Connor, of the Department of Physics at University College, Galway. He listened for a while and then said, 'It really is a medical problem.'

A medical problem that a man can sit in Kells, County Meath, and direct this energy, or whatever it is, to a place he has never been, never seen, getting this power to a thing as tiny as a vein, and stopping the bleeding?

Is thought energy? I persisted. Is willpower energy? This healer did not even have previous experience of attempting such a cure at a distance. Is it a form of telepathy?

Dr O'Connor's reply was straightforward. 'There is an area where physicists do not give an answer. We do not know what this thing telepathy really is. There is no physics theory at the moment to explain the phenomenon.

'There would be no problem with the timing, of course, because the speed of light, for instance, is very fast. It would be only a fraction of a second to Dallas. Speed is not a problem.'

So if this is also some kind of energy . . .?

'Yes, but we do not know what kind of thing this is.'

I probed a little further. How could it be directed with such precision? How could it get into the right room, and locate the haemorrhage?

Dr O'Connor: 'There is no explanation that I know of.'

<hr />

Carmelite priest Fr Aidan O'Donovan is well known in Ireland for his healing and caring, though he approaches healing a little differently from the gift healers. Where they heal through their gifts (although most also say a prayer as they heal), Fr O'Donovan heals only through prayer.

He is a man in a rush, like a river of faith in God, and is totally committed to the sick and the tired and the lonely. I persuaded him to tell me about his healing.

'I cannot deny I have the charisma,' he told me. 'The charisma is greater than the ministry of healing, and it is a gratuitous gift. All healing comes from God, and all I do is in the name of Jesus, Who bore all our infirmities.'

He dismissed the custom of putting the worm into the hand of a newborn seventh son: 'It has nothing to do with science or religion, so that leaves only superstition.'

But why has the custom of putting a worm into the hand of the newly born seventh son before baptism persisted? Other once deeply held superstitions have long since been forgotten, overtaken by education and medical advances. One mother of a seventh son remembers putting the worm into her infant's hand. 'How could we not take the chance that Peter might have the cure?' she said to me. 'Besides, that is how it was always done.'

'But why bother?' I asked. 'There are plenty of cures for ringworm now. The doctors can cure it. It may take a bit longer, but they can do it.'

'I talked it over with my husband,' she said. 'But then we thought, what if Peter goes to Africa or some other country where there might be lots of ringworm, and there mightn't be doctors or drugs? What then?'

Then she added the clincher: 'He was entitled to his birthright.'

Lady Wilde includes the following prayer in her *Ancient Legends of Ireland*:[1]

> We kill a hound. I kill a small hound. I kill a deceitful hound. I kill a worm wherein there is terror: I kill all his wicked brood. Seven angels from paradise will help me, that I may do valiantly, and give no more time to the worm to live than while I recite this prayer.

The ancient serpent-idol was called, in Irish, 'the great worm', an ollphéist. Irish legend has it that St Patrick destroyed it, and had it thrown into the sea. There are now no snakes to be found in Ireland – not even grass snakes. Is it possible that the old ceremony of the child and the worm is the result of a muddled and patchy race memory of triumph over the great worm, a mockery, a celebration of its destruction at the hands of even an unbaptised baby?

If Fr O'Donovan were to visit Westport in County Mayo, he would meet a kindred spirit in the Revd John Heaslip, the Church of Ireland rector. He too is dedicated to healing through prayer, and agrees in condemning the practice of putting the worm into the hand of an unbaptised baby. They both refuse to take personal credit for curing people, and instantly correct the impression that they themselves are the healers. Both insist that God works through them.

The Revd Heaslip remembers both successes and failures in his healing ministry. 'You always have to balance one against the other,' he says. 'I've had some dramatic successes, and some dramatic failures. Nothing has happened in several cases.'

I asked for an instance of successful healing.

'One evening,' he told me, 'a colleague phoned to say she had been diagnosed as having cancer of the ovary and was to have immediate surgery to remove both womb and ovaries. At the time I was busy helping with a school play. I rushed over to her during the interval, and we prayed together. Our prayer was very simple: we asked God that He would give great skill and success to the surgeon. We also opened ourselves to the possibility that God would miraculously bring healing.

'When this woman came to after the anaesthetic, she found there had been no operation. There had been no cancer. I do not know what happened.

'But I do know I am nothing myself. The Holy Spirit works through me.'

Whether we like it or not, the Anglican rector and the Catholic priest are rarities in today's Christianity. Yet healing was a part of Christianity from the beginning. Most of the miracles performed by Jesus in the gospels were acts of healing, and many saints were canonised because of their healing abilities. The last action of Jesus as a free man was to heal the soldier whose ear Peter had cut off.

Why and how has healing, so important to early Christianity, declined in importance. How has it been left to the occasional seventh son of a seventh son, or to the rare holy priest, be he Anglican or Catholic?

I went to see theologian Fr Gabriel Daly, of Trinity College, Dublin. I asked him if he thought the power to heal had declined as the temporal power and wealth of the Church had grown.

Healing has certainly declined, he agreed, but not died out entirely. 'I do not know if you can directly correlate the two – power and decline – because the healing in the New Testament belongs to that particular period; and temporal power in the Church did not arrive until well into the fourth century.

'But in every age there has been an awareness of prayerful healing in the Church, with some people more than others. I do not think there was ever a general practice of it, but particular needs were met. And there were always the thaumaturgists that people associated with healing. You will find them more in evangelical Protestantism than in Catholicism.'

Could it be, I asked, that, during the Crusades and the Inquisition and the witch hunts, the minds of people were so fixed on fear and punishment that they stopped looking to the Church for healing?

Fr Daly could find no connection here. 'There were always people who were regarded as wonder workers. They might have been saints or whatever, to whom cures were attributed. We have plenty of records of that, so I don't think it has ever fully declined. One also finds it today with Padre Pio and the great Marian shrines like Lourdes and Knock, that have associations with healing.

'I don't believe there was a golden age of healing that simply ended. We have, after all, a sacrament of healing in the Catholic Church. It used to be called Extreme Unction, but now is called the Anointing of the Sick. It has, of course, a biblical origin.

'We ought to make more of the Anointing of the Sick as a healing sacrament. The first thing is to detach it from the old idea that you got Extreme Unction when you were on the way out. That it was the end.

'However,' he added, 'it must not be seen as an alternative to medicine. It should not be some kind of faith healing or even sacramental healing, as an alternative to going to the doctor. That is dangerous and very bad theology.'

God, he said, works through doctors as much as He works in any other way. It is important not to look for miracles in the old sense of God interfering in everyday life: He intervenes, yes, but within the person and within those around him, using natural causes.

'There is healing of the mind as well as the body. One must be prepared to accept healing as part of one's whole life. Not just "I've got this pain here and I'm going to get it healed." I think healing has a spiritual background, and takes in the whole person.'

But what about actual miracle working?

'Holy people in every age were expected to do this kind of thing. But from the time of the scientific revolution in the seventeenth century we have learnt to think differently: we no longer think of God intervening from the outside, but more intimately, that he works from within.'

Thoughtfully he continued, 'At the same time, the Catholic Church makes use of miracles for canonisation. I have difficulty with that kind of thing.'

Can we ever recover the old ability to heal, that seems to have been so widespread?

'There is no going back to that sort of thing. Besides, we have to be careful about what it really was – what belongs in the context of faith and what may belong to the paranormal areas we simply do not understand. The psychosomatic is such an area, and the curious relationship between mind and body is still so unexplored, as is the interaction between the two. A lot of healing surely takes place in that area.

'In holistic medicine you no longer treat the knee or chest in isolation. You treat the patient. That is becoming more and more recognised, in a purely scientific way. It also happens to be good theology.'

❦

Dr Patrick Logan, in his book *Irish Country Cures*, offers an explanation for the healers who cure skin cancer:

> The essential ingredient in cancer plasters is arsenic. This may be added to lard or butter, and applied as a plaster. This plaster causes severe pain, because the arsenic will destroy all the tissues.
>
> Undoubtedly arsenic plasters could and did destroy certain skin growths. I knew an old man, a relative of mine, who had a dangerous-looking wart on his finger removed by a plaster. The fact that he lost his finger as a result did not shake his faith in the treatment.[2]

However, pharmacies no longer stock arsenic, nor have they for many years. Yet Leslie Deacon is still treating large numbers of people for skin cancer. He uses plasters, eggs, herbs.

So the questions pile up.

How does a healing gift remain dormant for perhaps a hundred years after the healer dies – remaining only as a shadowy family memory – then suddenly awaken in a descendant? And how is it that the new healer needs neither instructions nor training (which could not be got, anyway)?

Is it feasible that these gifts develop through serving other people? Can healers actually be empowered by the needs and expectations of their community?

How could Simon McDonagh at ten months cure eczema? Could his mother's wish to help the old man have connected her emotionally with her child, in such a way that she was enabled to borrow the child's gift?

Why is the number seven so special? Why does blind nature — if blind nature it is — respond to human expectation, and endow the seventh son or daughter with gifts, usually healing gifts?

People who heal through prayer believe the power they call on is God's, and that it is God who heals through them. The question arises - are some of the religious healer really gift healers? Would some of them heal if they had never heard of God, or never said a prayer?

Are these gifts part of nature — part of a world in which everything seems to have an opposite? There is hot and cold, wet and dry, there are mountains and valleys, light and darkness. Is it possible that there is a built-in law that requires nature to provide means of healing in a world where there is illness and injury?

And why are healers so close-lipped? Why will they not reveal their methods or the ingredients of their cures, even to their closest friends or relatives? A woman whose son had died, and whose entire family lives in the United States and will not be returning, told me she would bring her secret to the grave.

When she had been given the gift, the donor had said to her, 'Do not tell that to anyone until you are passing it on.'

There is no relative near, and no one to pass it on to, so it will die with her. Why the silence?

More than anything else, the question — what is the origin of the healing gifts?

Gift healers are not confined to Ireland, but are found throughout the world. European countries vary greatly in their attitudes to them. In Norway herbalists may be consulted by the public but, by law, may only treat patients for minor health problems. In Belgium, the existence of alternative medicine and gift healers seems to be officially ignored. Only qualified doctors may practise, and the same is true for pharmacists. One wonders if in fact such restrictions are enforced. In Austria, to operate as a gift healer is illegal.

Switzerland has the most relaxed attitude of any country from which I sought information. There is no official organisation for alternative medicine there, and legislation about gift healers varies from canton to canton. Britain permits registered herbalists to prescribe and treat people on the health service – if the patients choose them. A homeopathic hospital is also given official support. There is no official attitude to gift healers. Finland accepts that there are gift healers, but most of them are connected with sects of the Christian church. French law seems tolerant of gift healers generally, and the French are very enthusiastic about bonesetters. Bonesetters thrive in France, especially in rural areas.

Ireland does not formally recognise chiropractors, spinologists or herbalists, but puts no legal prohibition on persons practising as such. It is likewise for gift healers. In Ireland at least 20,000 people a year opt for treatment by gift healer. Are those 20,000 simply fools, last hopers, victims of charlatans? Those I met were mostly persons of intelligence, judgement and often good education. If we choose to put gift healing on trial, these would be on the jury. Generation after generation of them have already returned a verdict of confidence.

While I was meeting the healers in this book, I often wondered if it might not be wise for them to organise and seek some official recognition. I wondered why they had not done so.

Hindsight suggest it may be wiser not to. Organising would mean just that – meetings, committees, secretary, treasurer, public relations, and so on. Inevitably the question of fees would arise, with all that entails. Expenses would have to be covered, if only those of the officials, and slowly, perhaps, the strange innocence of these remarkable people might slip away and vanish.

The gift healers do not seek people out. Nor do they shut people out. They simply give freely to others what was freely given to them.

Notes

1. Lady Speranza Wilde, *Ancient Legends of Ireland*.
2. Patrick Logan, *Irish Country Cures*, p.102